IN CELEBRATION
OF FYNBOS

This book is dedicated to the youth of South Africa,
a new generation of people who will play a crucial role in the future of fynbos,
one of the country's treasured natural heritages.

CONTENTS

Foreword   5

Introduction   7

Fynbos in a nutshell   11

Agapanthus africanus – flower of love   12

Agathosma betulina – buchu   16

Aloe ferox – bitter aloe   20

Arctotis hirsuta – African daisy   24

Aspalathus linearis – rooibos   28

Brabejum stellatifolium – wild almond   32

Brunsvigia orientalis – candelabra flower   36

Burchellia bubalina – wild pomegranate   40

Carpobrotus edulis – sour fig   44

Chondropetalum tectorum – thatching reed   48

Cotyledon orbiculata – pig's ear   52

Crassula coccinea - scarlet crassula   56

Cyclopia genistoides – honeybush tea   60

Disa uniflora – red disa   64

Drosera capensis – sundew   68

Elegia capensis – horsetail reed   72

Ericaceae – the erica family   76

Erica cerinthoides – fire heath   80

Eriocephalus africanus – wild rosemary   84

Foeniculum vulgare – wild fennel   88

Gazania krebsiana – terracotta gazania   92

Gethyllis spiralis – kukumakranka   96

Haemanthus coccineus – April fool   100

Helichrysum crispum – everlasting   104

Leonotis leonurus – wild dagga   108

Lessertia frutescens – sutherlandia   112

Leucadendron argenteum – silver tree   116

Leucospermum cordifolium – pincushion   120

Leucospermum oleifolium – Overberg pincushion 124

Mentha longifolia – wild mint   128

Mimetes hirtus – marsh pagoda   132

Nivenia stokoei – blue star   136

Nymphaea nouchali – blue water lily   140

Nymphoides indica – floating heart   144

Olea europaea ssp. *africana* – wild olive   148

Ornithogalum thyrsoides – chincherinchee   152

Orphium frutescens – sea rose   156

Oxalis pes-caprae – sorrel   160

Pelargonium cucullatum –

    hooded-leaf pelargonium   164

Pelargonium tomentosum –

    peppermint-scented pelargonium   168

Phylica pubescens – featherhead   172

Proteaceae – the protea family   176

Protea cynaroides – king protea   180

Protea neriifolia – oleander leaf protea   184

Protea repens – sugarbush   188

Restionaceae – the restio family   192

Salvia chamelaeagnea – rough blue sage   196

Tulbaghia violacea – wild garlic   200

Watsonia borbonica – pink watsonia   204

Zantedeschia aethiopica – white arum lily   208

Glossary   213

Index of common names   215

Index of practical uses   217

Further reading & contacts   218

Practical information   219

Acknowledgements   220

Biographies   221

FOREWORD

When I first met Petra and Paul, I took them to the highest point of my farm where we all marvelled at the beauty of the scenery. I am very fortunate indeed to have found my piece of paradise amongst fynbos and hope to register a large portion of the land as a private nature reserve.

After reading *In Celebration of Fynbos* I felt so inspired by the gardening part of the book that I decided to become a hands-on fynbos enthusiast. I have never gardened with fynbos before, but will definitely give it a try. The book made me realise that instead of planting lavender near the entrance, I could also use wild garlic. It's waterwise and keeps the snakes at bay. But most importantly, I will contribute to the conservation of our natural heritage.

More than 1 400 species of fynbos plants are threatened due to human activities such as building, agriculture and the growing economic value of fynbos, resulting in an increased demand for the plants. Some species are traded purely for their gardening qualities, others for their medicinal properties, their culinary and decorative uses, or their magical powers. Personally, I believe one shouldn't touch nature.

Despite the growing interest in fynbos, it remains a mystery to many of us. Some species grow right under our noses without our realising it. And how many houses are built erasing all the fynbos on the plot out of ignorance, but also because of the sheer laziness of the builders?

In Celebration of Fynbos is a delightful way of making fynbos more accessible. Paul's artistic photography and Petra's inspirational writing add a fascinating dimension to the appreciation of this unique vegetation.

You will most probably want to try some of the exciting tips in this book, but for conservation's sake, instead of picking plants from the *veld*, find out which nursery sells them. If you take leaves from a silver tree, I suggest that for each leaf you take, you plant another tree.

Growing fynbos may be a challenge, but it's worth the try. By planting some in your garden, you also contribute to its conservation. Go for fynbos rather than a tropical garden. I hope that this book will inspire you as much as it has inspired me.

Other than this book, what better way is there than taking friends from the city for a walk in the *veld* to sensitise them to the beauty of fynbos? If then they still can't hear the music in nature, give up on them!

Valli Moosa
Former Minister of Environmental Affairs and Tourism, President of IUCN (The World Conservation Union)

INTRODUCTION

This book is a treasure trove of delightful bits of information and passionate photography. In sharing my exciting discoveries, I hope they will have the same effect on you as they had on me: rushing off to the nearest nursery, buying out their stock, re-landscaping my garden and dragging everyone in from far and near to experience the magic of the plants introduced to you in this book.

It all started when I was five months pregnant. I saw a spark in the starlit sky and fifteen minutes later, the whole mountain was on fire. It could have cost us our home had we not fought fiercely to save it. The next morning there was not a trace of colour left in our once-dense garden. There was not a living creature for as far as we could see except for the ants, which came out by the zillions. The whole mountain was dark and covered with soot.

Soon after, the fynbos started sprouting out of the blackness, transforming the mountain into a bouquet of joy. We have never seen as many flowers as during that spring. With each new sighting my amazement grew, and when Paul began photographing this floral explosion, I knew I would never again be able to ignore the inherent beauty of fynbos. What his images revealed changed my perception forever.

I went on a journey of discovery and marvelled at nature's most amazing creative designs and her impressive ingenuity when it comes to the survival of the species. At one stage, it felt like meeting a group of people and getting to know them – 'Let's see who you are' – or if Paul photographed a flower at the end of my research I would say, 'Wow, is that what you look like?'

You could compare this experience to arriving at a *dorpie* in the Karoo. You know nobody and it looks like nothing much is going on, but as you get to know the people and the way they live, and they invite you into their homes, you realise that there is actually a great deal going on. This *dorpie* in the middle of nowhere looks dormant from the outside, but is surprisingly vibrant within.

My adrenaline levels rise when I find out something new about how the Khoisan and the early settlers used a specific plant, or when I step into a farm stall and see a whole range of beauty products made from one of 'my' plants. It's like a spark of recognition – 'Hey, I know you!' – and suddenly it's no longer just a cosmetic item on the shelves. It has become an amazing gift from nature.

Visiting a rooibos tea farmer and joining him in his *bakkie* for an hour's drive on a challenging 4x4 track through a *kloof* was another eye-opener. It is the only way to get to the organic rooibos fields, something the farmer does several times a week to check on the crops and the workers. There I learnt how, still today, the seeds are collected from ant hills by the local people. I discovered that rooibos is a beautiful bush that grows without any irrigation under the baking sun. 'So this is how my cup of tea starts its journey to my table!'

When I now look at the wild garlic that has grown near my kitchen for a year or two, I suddenly realise that I can actually eat it, and even use it as a disinfectant or a tick repellent. I also understand now why this is one of the few places in the garden where we don't have moles.

The other day, when I had indulged in too much garlic bread, I thought, 'All right, let's see what the book says.' I went to make myself a strong cup of buchu tea and guess what? I felt much better.

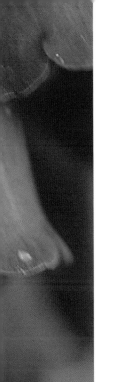

My research has also led me to some truly 'fynbos-addicted' people who have shared their passion with me and taught me to see the fun in fynbos – like eating protea seeds, feeding cheese crumbs to carnivorous plants and making love charms.

What I find most extraordinary in all this is how the passion for fynbos creates a bond between people. One day I visited an art gallery in Johannesburg and when I went back a year later, the owner vividly remembered me because we had both been so excited about the same fynbos flower.

I am so fortunate to have witnessed this incredible beauty and to have learnt so many exciting things about fynbos that I simply couldn't stop myself from sharing them with you.

I wish you much pleasure while reading this book, and still more when trying out some of the ideas.

Enjoy!

Petra Vandecasteele

IMPORTANT NOTE

Please consult your doctor or pharmacist before trying any of the health remedies included in this book.

Many fynbos species are protected by law, for the sake of conservation and to avoid over-picking, which has threatened some of the species with extinction. To collect plants in the wild, you need to apply for a permit at CapeNature – severe penalties are metered out for unauthorised picking. When buying plants, keep your receipts, and if you have received plants from a farmer or a friend, get a letter stating this. Apart from this, anything growing in your garden is yours, legally. The best is still to buy plants from licensed sellers, such as the botanical gardens.

Most of the plants in this book are fynbos in the strict sense of the word, others in a broader sense. The plants are shown in alphabetical order, not by category. The aim of this book is not to serve as a scientific tool to identify the plants, but to create awareness and to inspire.

Images that are not labelled show the main species under discussion. Where other species are shown, they are individually labelled.

See the disclaimer on page 223.

FYNBOS IN A NUTSHELL

At first sight, you might wonder what is so special about fynbos. As soon as you take a closer look, though, its exquisiteness is confirmed. There is only one way to appreciate fully the variety and the beauty of fynbos: you have to take your time and get in really close. Go down on your knees and check the plant at your feet – you're in for a pleasant surprise.

Fynbos literally means 'fine bush' and is a unique type of vegetation that accounts for more than 80 per cent of the plant species in the Cape Floral Kingdom. Over two-thirds of these plant species are not found growing naturally anywhere else in the world.

The Cape Floral Kingdom is the smallest of the six plant kingdoms in the world, and occupies a scant four per cent of South Africa's land, yet it is one of the earth's hot spots because of its exceptional biodiversity.

The Cape Floral Kingdom is three times smaller than the United Kingdom, but comprises six times more plant species and 290 times more endemic species. In fact, Table Mountain alone has as many plant species as the whole of the UK.

United Kingdom	Cape Floral Kingdom	Table Mountain
300 000 km^2	90 000 km^2	57 km^2
1 500 species	9 000 species	1 500 species

Of these 9 000 species, more than 1 400 are currently listed in the *Red Data Book* as being threatened. Housing, agriculture and over-picking are the main culprits.

Fynbos is represented by approximately 100 families. The three largest fynbos families are: the small-leaved ericas, the large-leaved proteas, and the grass-like restios.

Family	World	Cape Floral Kingdom
erica	4 500 species	670 species
protea	1 350 species	330 species
restio	400 species	320 species

Included in fynbos are more than 1 400 geophyte species, which propagate by means of underground buds.

LOVE

In the world of magic the *AGAPANTHUS* is a highly respected plant.

The roots can be used to make a love charm, and their magical powers even ward off thunder.

FLOWER OF LOVE

AGAPANTHUS AFRICANUS – FLOWER OF LOVE

NAME

Agapanthus means 'flower of love' and is derived from the Greek *agapé* meaning 'love' and *anthos* meaning 'flower'.

A. africanus and *A. praecox* are often confused. Both have medicinal properties, but it is *A. africanus* that is believed to be possessed of 'magical powers', whereas *A. praecox* is the one that enhances the beauty of our gardens.

IN THE GARDEN

Agapanthus is not only pretty, but also useful as a firebreak if planted near the house. You could plant this perennial en masse under trees to form a ground cover, on steep banks to hold the soil or along the front of a shrub border. Planted in containers, it makes a nice feature for a patio. It is hardy and requires little maintenance.

HEALING

Agapanthus contains several saponins (derived from the Latin *sapo* meaning 'soap'), which are toxic compounds that foam when shaken with water. Saponins have anti-inflammatory, antitussive and immuno-regulatory properties. They also help to reduce oedema or swelling.

The Zulu, following age-old traditions, use the roots and the leaves to treat respiratory problems, heart disease and chest pains.

Agapanthus is also the plant of fertility and pregnancy. Xhosa women use the roots for antenatal medicine, to induce labour and to make charm necklaces that are worn to enable the wearer to give birth to healthy babies.

TOXIC

❖ The sap of the leaves causes severe ulceration of the mouth.

SORE FEET

❖ Put some leaves in your hiking shoes for relief of swollen feet.

DECORATION

❖ *A. praecox* (another species in the *Agapanthus* genus) is an excellent cut flower.

❖ Use the whole head as it is, or wire it into a bouquet.

❖ Individual flowers can be used in small arrangements.

EASY TO GROW

A. africanus is hard to grow, while *A. praecox* is happy even in the poorest of soils. *A. praecox* is grown worldwide.

❖ Perennial – flowers in summer

❖ Needs average water – drought resistant

❖ Full sun

❖ Plant grows to 1 m

❖ Propagated from seed or by division

❖ Will grow in poor soil, but does best in well-drained, rich soil

❖ Tolerates light frost

❖ Good for shallow containers, mass displays, borders, rockeries and windy seaside gardens

❖ Use to stabilise banks to prevent erosion or as a firebreak

Agapanthus africanus – flower of love 15

A NOBLE'S TEA

If not for its many qualities,
why else would wealthy Europeans of
the late 1700s have been willing to pay
the value of a whole sheep for
a handful of buchu leaves?

BUCHU

AGATHOSMA BETULINA – BUCHU

NAME

Agathosma is derived from the Greek agathos meaning 'pleasant' and osme meaning 'smell'. The common name, buchu, comes from the Khoisan bookoo.

IN THE GARDEN

When the seed boxes start opening and you can spend some time right next to them, you will hear the 'pop-pop' of the seeds as they are powerfully expelled from their capsules. See how far they have been catapulted and you will be amazed at the strength of what lies within.

HEALING

The Khoisan were aware of the antiseptic and diuretic properties of A. betulina, which was most commonly used to treat respiratory, urinary, dermatological and digestive troubles. This aromatic herb was also believed to increase longevity. Today buchu is sold worldwide as seasoning and as an essential ingredient in a variety of homeopathic remedies.

COSMETICS

The Khoisan mixed the crushed leaves with fat from sheep's tails to perfume their bodies. The essential oils are now also used in perfumery.

COOKING WITH BUCHU

The plant's essential oils are great flavourants for jams and ice cream.

DID YOU KNOW

- ❖ Rub twigs of the buchu plant *Coleonema album* between your hands to remove fish smells.
- ❖ Buchu is a natural insect repellent when rubbed onto bedding or skin.

BUCHU BUTTER SAUCE

50 g butter – 25 g dried buchu leaves – 10 g flour – 25 ml fresh lemon juice – 50 ml double cream (makes 4 portions)

- ❖ Melt butter over low heat – add buchu leaves and sauté lightly – add flour and stir in quickly – add lemon juice and cream – simmer – serve immediately.
- ❖ Goes well with kingklip coated with masala spice.

SUNDOWNER

- ❖ Add ½ tot each of buchu brandy and sugar syrup to a flute of champagne.

BUCHU BRANDY OR VINEGAR

- ❖ Put a few thumb-length sprigs of fresh *A. crenulata* (another species in the *Agathosma* genus) in a bottle of brandy or white vinegar – add a couple of garlic cloves (optional) – shake daily for a week. Store in a cupboard.
- ❖ If you find the aroma too pungent, dilute the brandy with an ice cube.

HEALING

- ❖ Help for hangovers: add one teaspoon of buchu leaves or a buchu tea bag to a cup of boiling water.
- ❖ A tot of buchu brandy as a nightcap is said to stimulate good health.
- ❖ Drink buchu tea or brandy to aid digestion.

DECORATION

- ❖ Lovely in potpourri

CHALLENGING TO GROW (*A. OVATA*)

- ❖ Perennial – flowers in spring
- ❖ Waterwise – drought resistant – full sun
- ❖ Shrub grows to 1.75 m
- ❖ Propagated from seed or cuttings
- ❖ Likes well-drained, humus-rich soil
- ❖ Good for borders, edges, pots and herb gardens
- ❖ Attracts bees and butterflies
  TIP Plant after first rains.

Agathosma ovata

Agathosma crenulata

Agathosma betulina – buchu 19

H$_2$O

MOISTURE IS ALL.

THE ALOE'S FLESHY LEAVES CONTAIN LOADS
OF IT AND ARE ONE OF NATURE'S TRUE GIFTS
– TO NOURISH YOUR SKIN, TO HEAL YOUR
BODY AND TO SATISFY YOUR APPETITE.

BITTER ALOE

ALOE FEROX – BITTER ALOE

NAME

Aloe is the Greek word for the dried juice of aloe leaves; *ferox* means 'fierce' and alludes to the hard, spiny edges of the leaves.

IN THE GARDEN

Bitter aloe is a true asset to any garden. Sunbirds, weavers, starlings and mousebirds will all pay flying visits to your garden for the nectar, as will insects which will attract yet more birds. Moreover, its fleshy leaves contain plenty of moisture so the plant is slow to catch fire and serves well as a firebreak.

COOKING WITH BITTER ALOE

Who hasn't heard of *konfyt* (preserves) in South Africa?

HEALING

Through age-old methods, a bitter yellow juice is collected from cuts in the surface of the leaves. It is concentrated by boiling it until a dark-brown lump is formed, called 'Cape aloes', which is traditionally used for its laxative properties and as an ingredient in 'Schweden bitters'.

COSMETICS

In early days, young Swazi men used a mixture of aloe ash and soap to bleach their hair. People also rubbed powdered Cape aloe onto their faces to lighten their skin.

Today there is a wide variety of natural cosmetics ranges using aloe gel because of its capacity to hydrate and rejuvenate the skin as well as hair.

CULINARY TIPS

- ❖ To eat raw leaves, peel them and chop them into chunks (the bitterness is in the thick skin, with a sweet substance left underneath).
- ❖ It makes delicious *konfyt*.

SKIN CARE

- ❖ Split or crush fresh leaves and apply onto open wounds. This is also used to heal rashes, sores and burns.
- ❖ Mix powdered Cape aloes with Vaseline™ and apply to herpes and shingles.

LAXATIVE

- ❖ Take the equivalent size of a peppercorn of the raw product orally.

DECORATION

- ❖ Use the sturdy, dry flower stalks for floral arrangements that will last for years.
- ❖ Allow the flowers to dry slowly (this can take months) and naturally on the plant before carefully removing them. To speed up the process, remove all capsules.

EASY TO GROW

- ❖ Perennial – flowers in late summer
- ❖ Waterwise – drought resistant – full sun
- ❖ Grows up to 2 m in height
- ❖ Propagated from seed or offsets
- ❖ Grows in poor soil, but best in good soil
- ❖ Tolerates wind and light frost
- ❖ Good in walls and rockeries
- ❖ Used as a firebreak or accent plant
- ❖ Attracts birds and insects

  TIP Placed horizontally into a near-vertical rock face, the aloe will soon turn its stems and crowns upward.

ONLY YOU

African daisies are like women –
selective in their way of
showing affection.

They reveal their beauty only at the
sight of their true love – the sun.

African daisy

ARCTOTIS HIRSUTA – AFRICAN DAISY

NAME

Arctotis stems from the Greek *arctos* meaning 'bear' and *otis* meaning 'ear', referring to the big fluffy tufts of hairs on the fruit that resemble a bear's ears. The Latin word *hirsuta* refers to the soft, hairy leaves.

IN THE GARDEN

Just as mothers protect their children, the flower heads close in overcast weather to protect the pollen from rain.

Tough, easy and fast-growing are attributes on the wish list of many gardeners. Add to this a floriferous quality with large flowers in a range of colours and it is understandable why the African daisy is a popular ground cover across the globe.

Plant African daisies in a sunny rockery or use them as edging along an informal border. It is really worth planting, especially when you have a strandveld garden, as it tolerates high wind speeds and loose, sandy soil. It will put on a stunning display in the flowering season.

DID YOU KNOW

❖ To protect the seed, the flower heads bend down until their seeds are ready to be transported by the wind.

EASY TO GROW

❖ Annual – flowers in spring
❖ Likes a medium amount of water – full sun
❖ Compact ground cover – grows up to 40 cm in height
❖ Propagated from seed or cuttings
❖ Likes well-drained, sandy soil
❖ Tolerates wind; does not tolerate frost, but will re-sprout

Arctotis acaulis

Arctotis hirsuta – African daisy 27

POOR MAN'S COFFEE

IN THE 1950S, ROOIBOS TEA WAS A
SUBSTITUTE FOR COFFEE FOR THE POOR
RURAL COMMUNITIES IN THE CEDERBERG.
IT HAS NOW BECOME AN INTERNATIONALLY
KNOWN HEALTH BEVERAGE.

ROOIBOS

ASPALATHUS LINEARIS – ROOIBOS

NAME

Rooibos (literally 'red bush') gets its name from the dark red colour of the bushes when they are dead or after fermentation.

EXCLUSIVELY SOUTH AFRICAN

The incredible economic value of rooibos lies in the fact that it refuses to grow anywhere else than in certain parts of the Western Cape. Many countries have tried to grow the plant, but in vain. Rooibos is and stays a truly South African treasure.

FROM BUSH TO BAG

After being cut by hand, the leaves and branches are left to sweat (ferment), which gives the tea its colour and distinctive flavour. They are then dried, dusted and steamed to kill bacteria, before being dispatched worldwide. From having no market value, rooibos has turned into a thriving commodity.

COOKING WITH ROOIBOS

Rooibos adds flavour and health-giving properties to culinary efforts. On the shelves of supermarkets you will find cherry- or vanilla-flavoured rooibos, or blends with jasmine and fennel, to name just a few. The 'green' rooibos is the unfermented tea.

COSMETICS

Rooibos-based skin care products and toiletries are on offer at pharmacies and beauty parlours. According to the French, hair lotions containing rooibos may increase the speed of hair growth and reduce hair loss. It's worth a try, isn't it?

HEALING

The Khoisan used rooibos to aid digestion and treat skin problems. Its powerful antioxidants and a wealth of essential minerals protect against cell damage and disease, and are thought to slow down ageing. Rooibos is free of caffeine and tannin.

DID YOU KNOW

❖ *A. linearis* is one of approximately 278 species worldwide in the genus *Aspalathus*, which is the second largest genus in the Cape Floral Kingdom.

ICE CREAM

❖ See recipe on page 171.

DRINKS AND FOOD

❖ Replace water with rooibos tea in recipes for soups, marinades, sauces, stews and cakes for added flavour and nutrition.

❖ Use as a thirst-quencher. Its mineral content makes it a great sports drink.

❖ Mix with fruit juices to make iced tea.

❖ Steep for 5–10 minutes to increase antioxidant activity.

❖ Substitute hot coffee with hot rooibos tea to make 'Red Irish' instead of Irish coffee.

HEALTH – ADULTS

❖ Drink two cups of tea a day to boost your immune system, counteract anxiety, enhance your metabolism, fight allergies or simply for good health.

❖ Drink it straight to relieve hangovers and indigestion.

❖ Place a wet tea bag onto skin to relieve sunburn and itchiness.

HEALTH – CHILDREN

❖ Use organic rooibos tea bags to treat nappy rash and eczema, or add rooibos tea to the baby's bath water.

❖ Organic rooibos tea offers relief to colicky babies.

❖ For a cheap and natural electrolyte solution for diarrhoea and vomiting, boil 1 litre water and add 2 rooibos tea bags, 7 tsp of sugar and ¼ tsp of salt.

❖ Rooibos tea is a healthy supplement for babies who are allergic to milk.

DYEING FABRICS

❖ Soak fabric in rooibos tea to give it a delightful reddish-brown colour.

FAME

THE WILD ALMOND MADE HISTORY WHEN
IT WAS USED TO FORM THE FIRST FORMAL
BOUNDARY BETWEEN THE INDIGENOUS
PEOPLE OF THE CAPE AND THE NEWLY
ESTABLISHED CAPE COLONY.

WILD ALMOND

BRABEJUM STELLATIFOLIUM – WILD ALMOND

NAME

Brabejum stems from the Greek *brabeion* meaning 'sceptre' and possibly alludes to the position of the flowers on the plant. It might also refer to the leaves and the *brabeion,* or crown of bay leaves, which was awarded as a prize at games in Delphi. *Stellatifolium* is derived from the Latin *stellate* or 'like a star'. The fruits look similar to the almond and share its bitter taste.

IN THE GARDEN

The wild almond is perhaps not the prettiest of the proteas, but it attracts many a visitor. Insects and birds are lured by the sweetly scented flowers, and the fruits are treasured by porcupines and squirrels who are not sensitive to their toxic substances. The fruits float so that they can be dispersed by water. If they do not quickly establish themselves and germinate before the first rains, they perish.

A SNIPPET OF HISTORY

The wild almond first became famous as Van Riebeeck's Hedge, the first formal boundary between the European colonists and the Khoikhoi more than 300 years ago. The trees also became a focal point in a dispute over territory between the two parties. The Khoikhoi claimed a number of these trees or at least access to them so that they could collect the fruits and dig up the roots for winter food. This petition was not granted by the Dutch. Part of this hedge can still be seen today in Kirstenbosch National Botanical Garden and is now a heritage site.

COOKING WITH WILD ALMOND

The Khoisan ate the fruits and the roots. To leach out the poison, they soaked the fruits in water for several days, then boiled and roasted them. The early settlers copied the Khoisan and ground the roasted fruits in a desperate effort to make a coffee substitute.

DECORATION

In earlier days, the red and reticulated timber was popular for ornamental work. It was also used to make the heels of Dutch shoes, bowls, wagon felloes and brake blocks. The early settlers used the bark for tanning.

DID YOU KNOW

- ❖ The wild almond is not an almond at all but a member of the protea family.
- ❖ *B. stellatifolium* is the only member of the genus *Brabejum*.

TOXIC

- ❖ The fruits are poisonous, especially when eaten fresh.

AN ORGANIC JUNGLE GYM

- ❖ If you have an old wild almond in your garden, you could convert it into a fairy playground. The kids will love it!

CHALLENGING TO GROW

- ❖ Perennial – flowers from December to January
- ❖ Needs lots of water – full sun
- ❖ Tree grows to 8 m
- ❖ Propagated from fresh seed
- ❖ Needs permanently damp soil – likes stream banks
- ❖ Needs lots of space
- ❖ Used as a hedge
  TIP Water well during the first two years.

Brabejum stellatifolium – wild almond 35

SURPRISE

THE LARGE PINKISH 'EGGS' POP OUT OF THE GROUND WITHOUT A SINGLE LEAF IN SIGHT. IMMEDIATELY, THE PLANT STARTS TO GROW AND WILL SOON BE CROWNED WITH THE MOST AMAZING SPHERICAL FLOWER HEAD.

EMERGING IN LATE SUMMER IN THIS MOST BIZARRE WAY, IT COMES AS A TOTAL SURPRISE.

CANDELABRA FLOWER

BRUNSVIGIA ORIENTALIS – CANDELABRA FLOWER

NAME

The name *Brunsvigia* honours the House of Brunswick. *Orientalis* means 'from the east'.

The common names of this plant refer either to the candelabra-like shape of the flower or to its flowering time. Some names are lovely examples of how expressive common names can be, like *perdespookbossie*, meaning 'a plant that scares the living daylights out of the horses' or sore-eye flower, 'a flower that hurts your eyes if you stare at it too long'.

IN THE GARDEN

The pleasure doesn't stop once the candelabra flower has emerged in its spectacular way. The enormous flower head, which can be as wide as 600 mm in diameter, comprises between 20 and 80 flowers, to the utter delight of sunbirds. While they treat themselves to a good serving of nectar, these flying visitors are also offering a great pollinating service to the plant.

SURVIVAL

Candelabra flowers only emerge shortly before the first drops of rain in winter. The leaves will wait to appear until the flower has finished blooming so that the plant doesn't lose too much water at a time. For the rest of the year, the plant goes into a 'summer sleep' by resting underground as a bulb.

DID YOU KNOW

❖ If the flower head doesn't break off straight away, the seed will germinate in the head instead of waiting until it falls on the ground. When the seed is ready to germinate, it does so without delay, so you can't store it.

DECORATION

❖ Use the flower heads as an unusual centrepiece in your home.

CHALLENGING TO GROW

❖ Perennial – flowers in late summer to autumn
❖ Likes a medium amount of water – full sun
❖ Grows to 300 mm
❖ Propagated from seed, offsets and scales
❖ Likes good, loose, well-drained soil
❖ Tolerates wind and light frost
❖ Good for pots and rockeries
❖ Attracts birds

TIP It doesn't like being moved and must not be watered when dormant.

SMALL IS BEAUTIFUL

LUCKILY A SMALL TREE LIKE THE WILD POMEGRANATE IS EASY TO PROPAGATE, BUT IT GROWS RATHER SLOWLY.

ITS ROOTS ARE USED TO CONCOCT LOVE CHARMS, SO DON'T WASTE ANY.

WILD POMEGRANATE

BURCHELLIA BUBALINA – WILD POMEGRANATE

NAME

B. bubalina was named after W.J. Burchell, an early explorer and naturalist who travelled extensively in South Africa.

Bubalina is Latin for 'buff coloured'. It is likely that the name refers to the yellowish hairs as well as the buffalo-like horns of the mature calyx found on the fruit.

Its common name, wild pomegranate, refers to the slight resemblance of the tree in full bloom to the true pomegranate.

IN THE GARDEN

The wild pomegranate is an excellent garden tree that attracts many nectar-feeding birds. It is not only our feathered friends who love this small tree – anyone with a garden will appreciate its combination of bright red flowers and shiny, dark green leaves.

HEALING

In traditional healing, the roots serve as an emetic to cleanse the body.

COSMETICS

In Swaziland, infusions made of the roots are used as a traditional body wash.

DECORATION

In the past, the wood was a much-appreciated material for building huts and making agricultural tools.

DID YOU KNOW

- ❖ *B. bubalina* belongs to the coffee family, the *Rubiaceae*.
- ❖ This is a monotypic genus (that is, there is only one species in the genus).

DECORATION

- ❖ Good for flower arrangements
- ❖ The wild pomegranate has become increasingly popular as a small ornamental garden tree.

EASY TO GROW

- ❖ Perennial – flowers from spring till summer
- ❖ Likes a medium amount of water – full sun
- ❖ Shrubby tree grows to 3 m
- ❖ Propagated from seed or cuttings
- ❖ Tolerates wind and light frost
- ❖ Good for coastal gardens
- ❖ Attracts birds

  TIP It thrives on plenty of rain and doesn't like conditions that are too dry.

A JACK OF ALL TRADES

IT HIDES YOUR UNSIGHTLY SLOPES, FIREPROOFS YOUR GARDEN, LOOKS AFTER YOUR HEALTH *AND* PUTS FOOD ON THE TABLE.

SOUR FIG

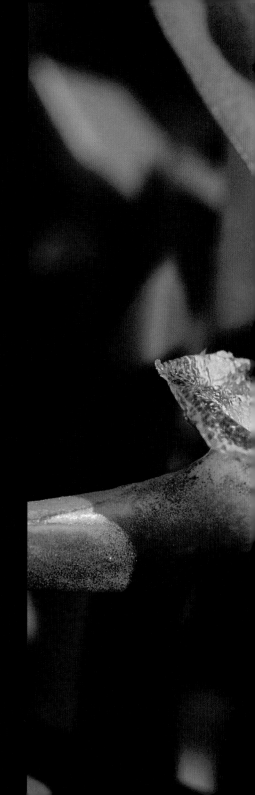

Carpobrotus edulis – SOUR FIG

NAME

Carprobrotus is derived from the Greek *karpos,* which means 'fruit', and *brotos,* which means 'edible'. *Edulis* is Latin for 'edible'.

IN THE GARDEN

Few plants can beat the sour fig when it comes to covering unattractive embankments quickly and successfully. Planted worldwide, it has more to offer than just being a ground cover. This fleshy-leaved plant is an excellent fire-retarding gem that can be planted in big patches close to the house.

COOKING WITH SOUR FIGS

Well known for its culinary properties, the sour fig is extensively harvested. It is extremely popular with rural communities who sell it in packets on the roadside. You will also find the dried fruit in Cape Town's many informal markets, waiting for buyers to use as an ingredient in Eastern dishes or in delicious preserves and curries.

HEALING

The highly astringent juice of the leaves has traditionally been used as an antiseptic to treat ailments as well as digestive and skin problems. It also helps to stop bleeding.

FINGER FOOD

- ❖ Eat the fruit raw by simply biting off the bottom of the ripe seed capsule and sucking out the syrupy contents.

 INTERNAL USES

- ❖ Use an extractor to get the juice out of the leaves.
- ❖ For oral infections, gargle with the juice.
- ❖ For digestive troubles, drink the juice.
- ❖ For tuberculosis, earache, toothache and vaginal thrush, drink the juice.

 SKIN CARE

- ❖ For healing of wounds and burns, or to treat eczema, apply the juice or pulp to the skin.
- ❖ For neutralising insect bites and bluebottle stings, apply the juice to the bite.

 EASY TO GROW

- ❖ Perennial – flowers in spring
- ❖ Waterwise – drought resistant – full sun
- ❖ Ground cover
- ❖ Propagated from division or from cuttings
- ❖ Tolerates poor soil
- ❖ Tolerates wind and light frost
- ❖ Good for embankments as pioneering ground cover on steep slopes and in rockeries
- ❖ Used as a firebreak and to prevent soil erosion

  TIP It needs no special care, but must be kept under control.

Carpobrotus edulis – sour fig 47

Ikebana

IN EMPHASISING THE LINEAR ASPECTS OF
THE CONSTRUCTION, JAPANESE FLOWER
ARRANGERS MAKE FASCINATING USE
OF THATCHING REED.

THATCHING REED

CHONDROPETALUM TECTORUM – THATCHING REED

NAME

Chondropetalum is derived from the Greek *chondros* meaning 'cartilage' and *petalum* meaning 'petal'. *Tectorum* is Latin for 'roofing', alluding to the plant's use as a thatching material.

IN THE GARDEN

Thatching reed makes a lovely feature plant for waterwise gardens. It is happy in a wide range of soil types and in many climatic zones.

A SNIPPET OF HISTORY

Fynbos has always provided shelter and food for the nomadic Khoikhoi. During their extended stays at good grazing or fishing sites, they would build temporary shelters from tall restios, called *kapstylhuise* by the *trekboere* (nomadic farmers).

The early settlers soon began to appreciate the value of the durable thatching reed as roofing material for their houses, knowing that it would last 20 years or more.

Over time, thatching reed has been replaced by longer-lasting, less flammable materials.

DECORATION

❖ In ikebana, the stems of the thatching reed are much sought after to create stylish compositions.

CHALLENGING TO GROW

❖ Perennial – flowers in winter
❖ Waterwise – drought resistant – full sun
❖ Grows to 1.5 m
❖ Propagated from seed or by division
❖ Grows in a wide range of well-drained soil, loves marshes
❖ Tolerates wind and light frost
❖ Good for coastal gardens

TIPS Treat the fragile seeds with smoke to stimulate germination. The plant does not tolerate pruning, so choose a variety that will not grow too tall for its location. Plant at the beginning of the rainy season. Do not add fertiliser when planting as it might burn the roots. It needs plenty of air movement.

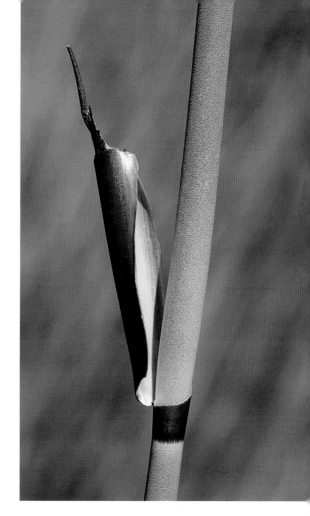

Chondropetalum tectorum – thatching reed 51

MAGIC

THE SOUTHERN SOTHO MAKE
PROTECTIVE CHARMS FOR ORPHAN
CHILDREN FROM THE DRIED
LEAVES OF THE PIG'S EAR.

PIG'S EAR

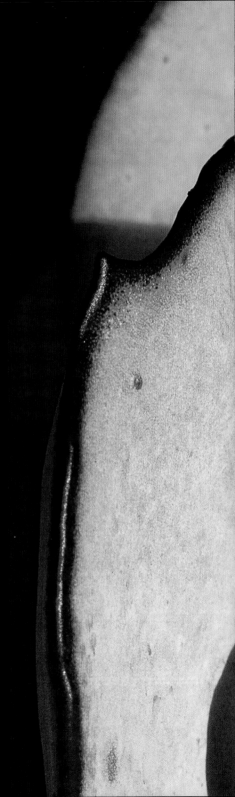

COTYLEDON ORBICULATA – PIG'S EAR

NAME

Cotyledon stems from the Greek word *kotyledon* meaning 'cup-shaped hollow'. *Orbiculata* is Latin for 'round circle'. The common name, pig's ear, refers to the oval shape of the leaves.

IN THE GARDEN

Pig's ear adds colour to gardens in winter and will attract birds for many months due to its long flowering period.

The powdery white coating not only adds attractive colouring to the silver-grey leaves, but possibly reflects a great deal of the sun's heat to prevent loss of moisture.

HEALING

Pig's ear is well known in traditional healing and is a widely utilised medicinal plant used to expel worms and to treat skin problems and a variety of other ailments. Its toxic principle, cotyledontoxin, acts as a local anaesthetic.

DID YOU KNOW
- ❖ Pull the bark from the stem, blow through it and you will hear the call of a young duiker.

TOXIC
- ❖ The more moisture the leaves contain, the more toxic they are. Never use internally unless prescribed by a medical doctor.

SKIN CARE
- ❖ To soften and remove hard corns and warts, apply the fleshy part of the leaf and hold with plaster.
- ❖ For blisters, apply the skin of the leaves.

EARACHE
- ❖ In traditional healing, the juice is heated and used externally as ear drops.

EASY TO GROW
- ❖ Perennial – flowers in winter or midsummer (Western Cape)
- ❖ Waterwise – drought resistant – full sun or semi-shade
- ❖ Shrub grows to 1 m
- ❖ Propagated from seed or cuttings
- ❖ Likes most well-drained, sandy soils
- ❖ Tolerates light frost
- ❖ Good for pots, rockeries and borders
- ❖ Used as a firebreak and in dry areas
- ❖ Attracts bees and birds

  TIP Do not over-water newly planted seeds.

Cotyledon orbiculata – pig's ear 55

ROCK CLIMBER

THE CHERRY ON THE CAKE OF A HIKE ON
TABLE MOUNTAIN IS WITHOUT A DOUBT THE
SIGHT OF THE BRILLIANT SCARLET CRASSULA
HANGING FROM THE CLIFFS.

SCARLET CRASSULA

CRASSULA COCCINEA – SCARLET CRASSULA

NAME

Crassula stems from the Latin *crassus*, meaning 'thick', and refers to the fleshy leaves. *Coccinea* means 'deep red'.

IN THE GARDEN

The fast-growing scarlet crassula is an excellent waterwise plant and a lovely garden feature, not only for its showy flowers, but also for its decorative leaves. It will attract the Table Mountain Beauty butterfly, which pollinates it. Well equipped with a really long tongue to suck the nectar out of the crassula's narrow flowers, this large chocolate-brown butterfly visits and pollinates only flowers with the same shade of scarlet as *C. coccinea*.

DID YOU KNOW

- ❖ Butterflies are not commonly found visiting fynbos.
- ❖ The scarlet crassula has only one pollinator, the Table Mountain Beauty butterfly.

EASY TO GROW

- ❖ Perennial – flowers from summer till autumn
- ❖ Waterwise – drought resistant – full sun
- ❖ Grows to 50 cm
- ❖ Propagated from seed or cuttings
- ❖ Tolerates poor soil, but prefers well-drained, sandy soil
- ❖ Does not tolerate frost
- ❖ Good for rockeries, pots and beds
- ❖ Attracts butterflies

Crassula coccinea – scarlet crassula 59

SWEET TEMPTATION

FROM AS EARLY AS THE 1700S, COUNTRY FOLK HAVE BEEN CAPTIVATED BY THE LOVELY AROMA OF HONEYBUSH TEA.

HOWEVER, IT IS ONLY IN MORE RECENT TIMES THAT PACKETS OF HONEYBUSH TEA HAVE BECOME MORE WIDELY AVAILABLE.

HONEYBUSH TEA

CYCLOPIA GENISTOIDES – HONEYBUSH TEA

NAME

Cyclopia stems from the Greek *Cyclops*, a race of single-eyed giants in Greek mythology. It alludes to the intrusive base of the whorl, which contributes to the flower's unique appearance. *Genistoides* is named after the *Genista*, because of its resemblance to an upside-down broom.

IN THE GARDEN

The delightful honeybush with its distinctive yellow flowers is still a very new feature in the garden. The adventurous gardener should plant the young plants 1 m apart. If happy, they will grow fairly rapidly, but will look untidy if not pruned regularly.

IN THE VELD

This typical small fynbos shrub is easy to miss when not in flower, but in summer it betrays itself by its sweetly scented yellow pea flowers. Most of the pollination is done by money beetles, which are attracted to the flower's inviting aroma.

There are 23 species of *Cyclopia*, of which at least nine are used for tea. It used to be collected in the *veld*, but increasing demand for it pushed collectors further into inaccessible areas, making cultivation necessary.

COOKING WITH HONEYBUSH TEA

The tea is made from the shoots and leaves of the shrub.

HEALING

Drinking honeybush tea is said to promote good health and to stimulate the appetite. It is also a recommended drink when breast-feeding, as it is believed to stimulate the production of milk. High in antioxidants, it contains no caffeine and its tannin level of 0.45 per cent is much lower than that of Ceylon tea (15–30 per cent). The Khoisan drank the tea to treat respiratory ailments and diabetes.

DID YOU KNOW

- ❖ Honeybush was first mentioned in botanical literature in 1705.
- ❖ The first large-scale South African honeybush plantation started off in 2001 in Haarlem near Uniondale.

 DRINKS – IDEAS

- ❖ The pleasant sweet flavour is enhanced by boiling. Boil 3 heaped tablespoons of dried honeybush in 1 litre water and simmer for 20 minutes.
- ❖ Drink honeybush tea straight or add a little honey to enhance the original honey flavour.
- ❖ Blend with fruit juice, or chill and drink it plain.

 GENERAL HEALTH

- ❖ Drink two cups of honeybush tea a day for general good health.
- ❖ For respiratory problems, diabetes and menopausal discomfort, several cups of honeybush tea a day may offer relief.

 CHALLENGING TO GROW

- ❖ Perennial – flowers in spring
- ❖ Likes an average amount of water – full sun
- ❖ Bush grows to 80 cm
- ❖ Propagated from seed or cuttings
- ❖ Likes well-drained, sandy loam soil with low clay content, pH 3.6–5.
- ❖ Tolerates light frost
- ❖ Attracts beetles

  TIPS Eliminate pods that float. Abrade the coat of the seeds lightly with sandpaper or treat with smoke to stimulate germination.

Cyclopia genistoides – honeybush tea 63

Geisha

Charismatic yet fussy, exclusive and protected, the exquisite disa could not have been a better choice as the emblem of the Western Cape.

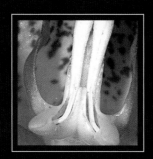

RED DISA

DISA UNIFLORA – RED DISA

NAME

Disa was named after the heroine of a Swedish legend by the Swedish botanist, Carl Peter Thunberg. He has been called 'the father of South African botany'. *Uniflora* means 'single flower'.

IN THE GARDEN

Although red disas will cope with hot summer temperatures of 30˚C if they receive enough water and fresh air, they prefer a cool environment (average 10–26˚C).

SOMETHING TO THINK ABOUT

The disa can be seen in nature on rock cliffs and in a few select gardens. It has also become a preferred icon or brand image for many companies, and appears on signage, rugby jerseys and letterheads, to name but a few. These are all examples of how popular the disa

has become. South Africa's famous red orchid is strictly protected, so why not take up the challenge of growing this 'temperamental prima donna' in your garden and contribute to its conservation?

SYMBIOSIS

All orchids, including the disa, produce zillions of small, dust-like seeds that are blown incredible distances by the wind. To enable the plant to grow, these minute seeds first need to develop a symbiotic relationship with a special kind of fungus in the soil. This fungus acts as a fine root system which delivers nutrients to the seedling. The orchid provides energy-rich carbohydrates in exchange.

COSMETICS

The oil of the disa is sold as a base product to the perfume industry.

DID YOU KNOW

- ❖ The large brown Table Mountain Beauty butterfly is the only known pollinator of *D. uniflora*.

DECORATION

- ❖ The disa is a fantastic cut flower with long-lasting qualities.

CHALLENGING TO GROW

- ❖ Perennial – flowers in summer
- ❖ Likes lots of water – semi-shade
- ❖ Grows to 60 cm
- ❖ Propagated from seed or by division
- ❖ Thrives in well-drained, coarse river sand
- ❖ Likes wet or moist conditions
- ❖ Tolerates wind and frost
- ❖ Good for pots in a tray of water
- ❖ Attracts butterflies

  TIPS The disa needs free air movement and good light. Never let the roots dry out but do not over-water. The pH of the water should be 5–6.8. Avoid using chlorinated tap water.

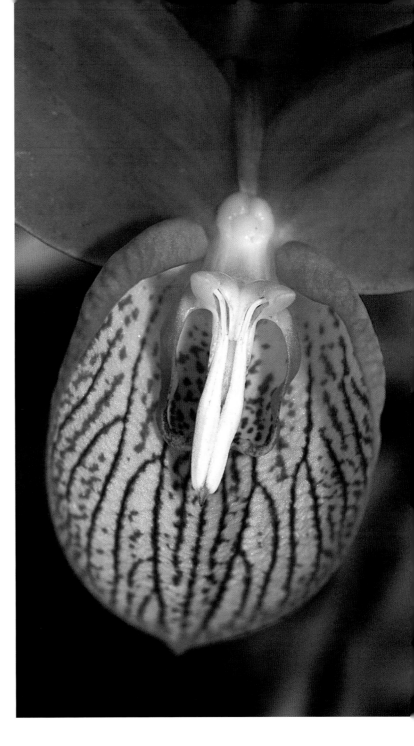

Disa uniflora – red disa 67

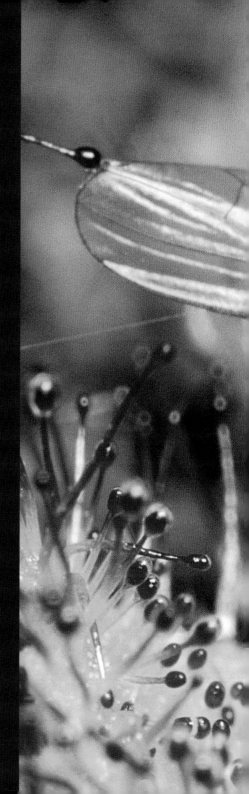

HAZARDOUS BEAUTY

You imagine that if you put your finger inside a sundew, it will grab it.

This won't really happen, unless you Are an unsuspecting insect.

Can you believe that this exquisite plant is a carnivore in disguise?

SUNDEW

Drosera capensis – SUNDEW

NAME

Drosera is derived from the Greek *drosos* meaning 'dew' and refers to the glistening drops on the leaves. *Capensis* means 'from the Cape'.

IN THE GARDEN

Sundews trap and digest insects on their tentacles, not to amuse themselves, but as a way of coping with the 'poverty' in nutrient-poor soils. Attracted by the honey fragrance of the plant, the insect will be trapped by up to 200 sticky glandular hairs on the leaf. Then the leaf will slowly curl up around its prey and release enzymes to digest this valued protein, a nutrient the plant needs for growth and reproduction.

TACTICS

The giant of this carnivorous plant world is *Roridula*, a genus found in the Western and Northern Cape. It is inhabited by an insect that is specially adapted to catch other insects found on the sticky hairs of the plant without getting trapped itself. In exchange for this free protein, the bug defecates on the leaves, thus providing a fertiliser that is much needed by the plant.

DID YOU KNOW

- ❖ The flowers of the sundew last only one day.
- ❖ South Africa is home to the largest carnivorous plant in the world, the *Roridula*, with a height of 2 m and leaves like steel traps.
- ❖ If you give the sundew on your windowsill a morsel of cheese, and if you don't have any living flies, the chances are that the plant will eat it.

CHALLENGING TO GROW – FRAGILE

- ❖ Perennial – flowers in summer
- ❖ Likes lots of water – full sun or semi-shade
- ❖ Grows up to 10 cm in height
- ❖ Propagated from seed
- ❖ Likes well-drained, moist soil
- ❖ Does not tolerate frost
- ❖ Can grow in swamps, good in window boxes

Drosera aliciae

Drosera aliciae

Drosera aliciae

PANACHE

When the unusual feathery reeds
with their papery sheaths and bracts
rustle in the wind, a soothing song is
carried throughout the garden.

HORSETAIL REED

ELEGIA CAPENSIS – HORSETAIL REED

NAME

Elegia comes from the Greek *elegeia*. It alludes to the rustling sound made by the papery sheaths when the wind blows. *Capensis* means 'from the Cape'.

IN THE GARDEN

The horsetail is one of the most beautiful Cape fynbos reeds. This elegant garden plant has been cultivated in South Africa since about 1974 and is now also grown in gardens in the south of England and in parts of the US. It grows in places where there are few wind-free days, so it makes sense that seed distribution is by the wind.

USES

Horsetail reed is not only lovely in decoration, but also useful bound together as a broom.

DID YOU KNOW

❖ What looks like the whorls of threadlike 'leaves' are not leaves, but small branches.

DECORATION

❖ The young stems are particularly decorative, and make interesting features in flower arrangements.

EASY TO GROW

❖ Perennial – flowers in late spring

❖ Lots of water – full sun

❖ Foliage plant grows to 2.5 m

❖ Propagated from seed or by division

❖ Likes moist, well-drained, sandy soil, but not clay

❖ Tolerates wind and light frost

❖ Good feature plant next to a pond or swimming pool

TIPS Water regularly. Treat seeds with smoke to stimulate germination. Plant at the beginning of the rainy season.

A Rainbow Nation

There are approximately 4 500 species of Erica worldwide. Of these, 670 occur in the Cape Floral Kingdom.

THE ERICA FAMILY

ERICACEAE – THE ERICA FAMILY

NAME

Erica comes from the Greek *ereiko* meaning 'to break', because the stems are brittle and break easily.

IN NATURE

Ericas come in all shapes and sizes, and in virtually all colour combinations except blue. They grow mainly along escarpments in the south-western Cape, but a few extend up the eastern mountain ranges into KwaZulu-Natal and Mpumalanga.

The only one that grows naturally all over the country is *E. cerinthoides*. It can also be grown in gardens, and so can the gorgeous *E. patersonii, versicolor, massonii* and *vestita*.

Erica massonii

- ❖ Evergreen, with needle-like foliage, ericas vary from ground covers to shrubs growing to several metres in height.

- ❖ They can be cultivated in gardens provided the following conditions are available: good drainage, sunlight, careful watering, good air circulation and sandy, acidic soil with a pH of 4–5.5.

- ❖ Never disturb the roots.

Erica plukenetii

Erica pulchella

KALEIDOSCOPE

THE EVER-CHANGING FORMS OF THE
BEAUTIFUL FIRE HEATH CREATE A DELECTABLE
VARIETY, TO THE UTTER DELIGHT OF THE
MALACHITE SUNBIRD.

FIRE HEATH

ERICA CERINTHOIDES – FIRE HEATH

NAME

The flowers and the way they are organised on the plant are very similar to the honey wort or *Cerinthe*, hence the name *cerinthoides*.

IN THE GARDEN

Fire heaths vary greatly not only in size, but also in the colour of the flowers and their hairiness. The shrubs can be bushy or thin, and can grow up to 1.5 m in height.

IN THE VELD

Fire heath is one of the few ericas that re-sprout from a woody rootstock after fire. Not only does it survive fire, it actually thrives on it and will be stimulated to flower at any time of the year, adding colour to an otherwise desolate landscape.

A SNIPPET OF HISTORY

In 1794, the popular fire heath appeared in England's *Botanical Magazine*. Francis Masson started the cultivation of *E. cerinthoides* in that part of the world.

❖ The sticky hairs on the flowers help to reduce evaporation of moisture during the hot summer months.

EASY TO GROW

❖ Perennial – flowers in late winter to spring
❖ Likes a medium amount of water – full sun
❖ Shrub grows to 1.5 m
❖ Propagated from seed or cuttings
❖ Likes light, well-drained, well-composted sandy soil that is also acidic (pH 5.5–6.7)
❖ Does not like lime or manure
❖ Tolerates wind and light frost
❖ Good for flat beds, rockeries and pots
❖ Attracts birds

TIPS Treat seeds with smoke to stimulate germination. Do not disturb the roots. Mulching is important to keep the soil moist. It also protects the roots.

Erica cerinthoides – fire heath 83

Snow White

BIRDS USE THE FLUFFY MINIATURE COTTON
HEADS WHICH ARE ATTACHED TO THE SEED
FOR NESTING.

THE EARLY SETTLERS ALSO KNEW
HOW SOFT THESE WERE AND USED THEM
TO STUFF THEIR PILLOWS.

WILD ROSEMARY

ERIOCEPHALUS AFRICANUS – WILD ROSEMARY

NAME

Eriocephalus stems from the Greek *erion* meaning 'wool' and *cephalus* meaning 'head', which is an allusion to the woolly seed heads, which look like cotton wool or snow.

The Afrikaans common name of this plant, *kapokbos* (meaning 'bush of snow'), is derived from the appearance of the seed heads.

IN THE GARDEN

Wild rosemary is probably one of the best-known plants in the Western Cape because of its grey foliage and distinct fragance when crushed.

HEALING

The Khoisan and the *trekboere* (nomadic farmers) made decoctions from wild rosemary to cure respiratory and stomach ailments, flatulence and colic, or to use as a diuretic.

SURVIVAL

This rosemary is incredibly well equipped to survive drought by limiting the loss of moisture. The needle shape and grey colour of the leaves, which reflect sunlight, the tiny hairs that cover the plant, and its aromatic oils all contribute to the plant retaining as much water as possible.

COOKING WITH WILD ROSEMARY

Wild rosemary is mildly spicy and goes well with a variety of meat dishes, such as springbok loin and ostrich fillet carpaccio.

TEA

❖ Add one sprig of wild rosemary to a cup of boiling water to make tea.

NAMAQUA BRANDY SAUCE

1 chopped onion – 2 sprigs wild rosemary (remove branches) – 2 cups (500 ml) Namaqua brandy – 2 cups (500 ml) cream (makes 5–6 portions)

❖ Sauté onion with wild rosemary – add brandy – simmer for ½ minute with lid on – add cream – reduce to a delicious creamy sauce.

HAIR CARE

❖ Wild rosemary has traditionally been used as a hair growth stimulant and conditioner. Boil one measure of sprigs in two measures of water for 10–30 minutes and allow to cool before using. Strain and mix with melted Vaseline™ (optional).

DECORATION AND POTPOURRI

❖ The fluffy white seed heads, which look like tufts of cotton wool, can be dried for decoration.
❖ The leaves can also be used for scented sachets and potpourri.

EASY TO GROW

❖ Perennial – flowers in winter
❖ Waterwise – drought resistant – full sun
❖ Shrub grows to 2 m
❖ Propagated from seed or cuttings
❖ Likes light, well-drained soil
❖ Tolerates wind and frost
❖ Good for hedges
  TIP Plant during wet winter months.

Refreshing

The lovely anise-like flavour of fennel
adds 'oomph' to salads
and a myriad fish dishes.

WILD FENNEL

FOENICULUM VULGARE – WILD FENNEL

NAME

Foeniculum stems from the Latin *faeniculum,* a diminutive of *faenum,* meaning 'hay'. *Vulgare* is Latin for 'common'.

IN THE GARDEN

Wild fennel, originally introduced from Europe in the 1700s, is a relatively short-lived perennial herb, which is usually grown as an annual and is easy to cultivate.

IN THE HOUSE

In the old days, people put the green stems of wild fennel under their mattresses to repel bedbugs and fleas.

COOKING WITH WILD FENNEL

The beauty of fennel is that there is no waste. The seeds are used as a condiment, the leaves for flavouring and the stems for eating raw or cooked, just like one would do with celery.

HEALING

Fennel was an important medicinal herb for early Anglo-Saxons, who used it to treat jaundice and biliousness. It is also an age-old diuretic.

DID YOU KNOW

- ❖ Wild fennel is a relative of the carrot.

CULINARY FLAVOURING AND DECORATION

- ❖ The tender young leaves provide a refreshing addition to salads.
- ❖ The other leaves flavour fish dishes, soups and stews.
- ❖ Keep the seeds for sauerkraut, breads and cakes, or purely to add as a delightful finishing touch.

CELLULITE

- ❖ Fennel tea may be beneficial as a diuretic and help to reduce cellulite.

DIGESTION

- ❖ Fennel seeds stimulate digestion; eat raw or roasted, whole or ground after a meal.

EASY TO GROW

- ❖ Perennial – flowers in summer
- ❖ Average amount of water – full sun
- ❖ Grows to 1 m
- ❖ Propagated from fresh seed
- ❖ Grows in any soil
- ❖ Tolerates wind

TIPS If flowering is prevented, the plant will last for up to two years. Let part of the plant run to seed when its vigour begins to decline. Two plants in a tub will provide ample leaves for the average family's needs.

Sunshine reggae

The exquisite gazania only opens fully when the light is bright enough.

It brings so much joy during the brief English summers that it has become one of the most popular bedding plants in British gardens.

TERRACOTTA GAZANIA

Gazania krebsiana – TERRACOTTA GAZANIA

NAME

The *Gazania* was named in honour of Theodor of Gaza, a translator of botanical works. Meaning 'riches' in Greek, *gaza* alludes to the riches in colour of the flowers and the abundance of the plant.

One of its nicknames, 'treasure flower', really comes as no surprise.

IN THE GARDEN

It is so easy to fall in love with gazanias. They come in a great variety of joyful colours and their flowers brighten up any garden for many months. In fact, gazanias are so easy to grow that they do as well in pots as they do in beds. The fact that one variety, the 'Daybreak Red Stripe', won a gold medal for its unique colour and abundance of blooms is easy to understand.

This flamboyant perennial is Namaqualand's trademark and one of the parent plants for the many *Gazania* hybrids found in nurseries.

SURVIVAL

Gazania has some special tricks to get through the dry summer months, when it shrivels to a bundle of dry curly leaves, appearing as if dead. This functions to minimise exposure to the hot sun and prevents loss of moisture through its leaves. The woolly underside of the leaves often points upwards to cool the plant down. With the first rains, the whole gazania plant swells almost instantly, its leaves become erect, and the flower buds emerge.

DID YOU KNOW

❖ Each fruit in the flower head – and there are about 25 of them per head – is covered with silky hairs to enable easy dispersion by wind.

CULINARY DECORATION

❖ Gazanias are edible – add some to a dish as a colourful finishing touch.

EASY TO GROW

❖ Perennial – flowers from spring till summer
❖ Waterwise – drought resistant – full sun
❖ Grows to 25 cm
❖ Propagated from seed – self-seeder
❖ No soil preference, but must be well drained
❖ Tolerates wind and light frost
❖ Good for rockeries, beds, pots and in masses as ground cover
❖ Attracts beetles, butterflies and herbivores

TIPS Don't over-water. It appreciates a little compost.

Gazania krebsiana – terracotta gazania 95

Climax

As if the fragrance of their
flowers were not intense enough,
kukumakrankas blow our minds with
their heavily scented edible fruit –
a much-sought-after gem indeed.

KUKUMAKRANKA

GETHYLLIS SPIRALIS – KUKUMAKRANKA

NAME

Gethyllis is thought to come from the Greek *gethyon* meaning 'bulb'. It refers to the bulb's long white sheathing tunics that surround the base of the leaves. *Spira* is Latin for 'coil'.

IN THE GARDEN

Growing kukumakrankas is easier said than done. The bulbs die easily if over-watered and some people reckon one should leave their cultivation to bulb specialists. Be that as it may, practice makes perfect ...

SURVIVAL

Designed to cope with the heat of summer, kukumakrankas bloom only for two or three days in midsummer (all at the same time), fruit in autumn and produce leaves only in winter when conditions become favourable.

COOKING WITH KUKUMAKRANKA

The fleshy cylindrical fruit is edible and used to flavour brandy liqueur or as a substitute for vanilla. In the old days, children were sent into the *veld* to search for the seeds. You couldn't easily see what looked like a yellow bean sticking out of the ground, but your nose would lead you to it.

HEALING

Kukumakranka brandy is a popular old Cape remedy for colic and indigestion. Would the irresistible fragrance have anything to do with it?

DID YOU KNOW

❖ The kukumakranka is rated as one of the most fascinating bulbs in southern Africa because of its unusual foliage, flowers and fruit.

BRANDY

❖ Throw a few ripe fruit into a bottle of *witblits* (distilled alcoholic liquor) or brandy and make your own liqueur.

TEETHING

❖ Infusions of the flowers are traditonally used to relieve teething discomfort.

SKIN

❖ Traditionally, kukumakranka was applied to boils, bruises and insect bites.

POTPOURRI

❖ Use the dried seed pods in potpourri.

CHALLENGING TO GROW

❖ Perennial – flowers in summer

❖ Likes medium water – drought resistant – full sun

❖ Needs well-drained soil

❖ Tolerates light frost

❖ Good for deep pots

TIP Stop watering as soon as the leaves begin to wither (in spring) and move pots to a cool dry place.

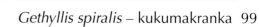

Gethyllis spiralis – kukumakranka 99

A FIRST

Believed to be the first flower collected from Table Mountain, the April fool was also probably the first South African flower to be mentioned in European literature.

APRIL FOOL

HAEMANTHUS COCCINEUS – APRIL FOOL

NAME

Haemanthus stems from the Greek *haima* meaning 'blood' and *anthos* meaning 'flower'. *Coccineus* is Latin for 'deep red'.

Two of its common names, April fool and March flower, refer to the flowering time, while other common names such as paintbrush lily and *velskoenblaar* refer to the appearance of the leaves. *Velskoene* is the Afrikaans name for shoes made from animal hide, and *blaar* is Afrikaans for 'leaf'.

IN THE GARDEN

When April fools appear in all their glory and all else has finished flowering, they look like fire. The intense colour will stop you in your tracks.

SURVIVAL

The April fool adapts to long dry summers by resting in the soil in the form of a large bulb. To prevent loss of moisture through transpiration of the leaves and flowers, the flower head pops up just before the first rains. Only later will the leaves appear so that loss of moisture is spread over time.

HEALING

In traditional healing, ulcers and sores were treated by applying a poultice of fresh leaves.

DID YOU KNOW
- ❖ The April fool bears only two large leaves.

TOXIC
- ❖ The bulb contains coccinine, an alkaloid with a convulsive action.

SKIN
- ❖ For septic ulcers and sores, apply fresh leaves as a dressing.

DIGESTION AND ASTHMA
- ❖ To make a diuretic, boil the sliced bulb in vinegar and mix with honey. The same mixture has traditionally been used to treat asthma.

CHALLENGING TO GROW – FRAGILE
- ❖ Perennial – flowers in late summer
- ❖ Waterwise – drought resistant – semi-shade
- ❖ Shrub grows to 20 cm
- ❖ Propagated from seed, offsets and scales
- ❖ Needs well-drained, sandy soil
- ❖ Tolerates light frost
- ❖ Good for pots or open ground
- ❖ Attracts sunbirds, noctuid moths and bees

TIPS Water well only once when seeding and every second week after the first leaves appear. Give plenty of water in growing season. This plant does not react well to any disturbance so choose a big enough pot from the start.

CALLING THE SPIRITS

In traditional ceremonies sangomas will dry *HELICHRYSUM*, bundle it together, and place it in old broken pottery to burn it. The aromatic smoke of the incense is inhaled to invoke the ancestors.

EVERLASTING

HELICHRYSUM CRISPUM – EVERLASTING

NAME

Helichrysum is derived from the Greek *helikhrusos* or *helix* meaning 'spiral' and *khrusos* meaning 'gold', referring to the bright yellow colour of the flower heads.

The Afrikaans common name, *sewejaartjie*, stems from the belief that the flower heads last for seven (*sewe*) years (*jare*).

IN THE GARDEN

Little by little, often over several weeks, the bright-yellow papery bracts of the everlasting buds open to reveal the darker yellow flowers in the centres. Rubbing the golden mass of flowers releases their delicate camphor scent.

SURVIVAL

The everlasting has quite an ingenious way of coping with extended dry periods. The grey colour of its foliage reflects the sunlight to reduce loss of moisture, while the woolly hairs and the narrow leaf shape minimise transpiration.

HEALING

The Khoikhoi traditionally used the everlasting as a calming tea and to treat various ailments.

COSMETICS

In skin care, it is valued for its anti-allergenic, anti-inflammatory, astringent and antioxidant properties. It is believed to stimulate regeneration and new cell growth. The oils are excellent for healing scars and acne.

HYPERTENSION AND DIABETES

❖ In traditional healing, infusions of everlasting are believed to help with hypertension and diabetes. Infusions are made by adding a handful of branches and leaves of *H. crispum* to 500 ml boiling water, letting it stand for 12 hours, and then straining it. Drink one cup in the morning and one at night.

DECORATION

❖ Fresh cut flowers last a long time.
❖ Dried cut flowers display a wide array of colours that don't fade.

POTPOURRI

❖ Its aroma makes it a lovely addition to potpourri.

EASY TO GROW

❖ Perennial – flowers in summer
❖ Medium water – drought resistant – full sun
❖ Plant grows to 1 m
❖ Propagated from seed or cuttings
❖ Likes any well-drained soil
❖ Tolerates wind and light frost
❖ Good for embankments, walls, rockeries and pots
    TIPS Do not over-water. Compost is appreciated.

Helichrysum petiolare

Helichrysum crispum – everlasting 107

EUPHORIA

IN THEIR ATTEMPT TO REVOLUTIONISE
AFRICAN DISHES, SOME RENOWNED CAPE
CHEFS USE WILD DAGGA TO FLAVOUR MEALS
AND CREATE A 'SEXY' AFRICAN FEEL. IT'S
INGENIOUS AND TASTY WITH
A TRULY SOUTH AFRICAN FLAIR.

WILD DAGGA

LEONOTIS LEONURUS – WILD DAGGA

NAME

Leonotis stems from the Greek *leon* meaning 'lion' and *otis* meaning 'ear'. The petals of the flowers form a typical whorl, which resembles the ear of a lion. *Leonurus* means 'lion coloured'.

A 'LEKKER' GARDEN

Birds, bees and butterflies just love the profusion of nectar of wild dagga flowers. Adding this easy-growing shrub to your garden means welcoming many flying visitors with a 'sweet tooth'. Considering the fact that wild dagga is known for its euphoric effects, your neighbours might wonder what you're up to ...

HEALING

The word 'dagga' is taken from the Khoikhoi word *dachab*. In traditional healing, wild dagga is used to treat fevers, headaches, coughs and dysentery. Decoctions are applied for the relief of haemorrhoids, eczema, skin rashes and boils. Added to the bath, wild dagga alleviates itching and muscular cramps. It is also used as a charm to keep snakes at bay, and has reputedly been used to treat snake bites.

WILD DAGGA PESTO

*2 cups (500 ml) fresh wild dagga leaves –
½ cup pine kernels – 2 cups (500 ml) fresh
coriander leaves – ½ cup (125 ml) freshly
grated Parmesan – 3 large garlic cloves
(crushed) – 125 ml grapeseed oil – salt and
pepper to taste (makes 4 portions)*

❖ Blanch wild dagga leaves in salted water – dip in
ice cold water to remove the bitterness – drain
and pat dry – toast pine kernels until golden
– cool and chop finely – puree all ingredients in
a food processor until smooth – keep chilled and
use within three days.

DECOCTIONS

Traditonally, decoctions are made with leaves,
stems and (sometimes) roots. Do not use this
without first consulting a medical practitioner.

❖ Add 10 g chopped dried herbs to 500 ml boiling
water – boil for 10 minutes – allow to cool
– strain and use the clear liquid for both internal
and external use.

❖ Infuse 20 g fresh young twigs to 1 litre boiling
water – allow to cool – strain.

❖ Adult dosage for internal use of infusion: 90 ml;
use half of this for elderly people.

EASY TO GROW

❖ Perennial – flowers profusely in autumn
❖ Waterwise – drought resistant – full sun
❖ Shrub grows to 2.5 m
❖ Propagated from seed or cuttings – self-seeder
❖ Likes good moist soil, loves loamy soil
❖ Tolerates wind and frost
❖ Good for coastal and inland gardens
❖ Attracts bees and sunbirds

TIPS Water well in summer, little in winter.
Compost is appreciated. Frequent trimming
stimulates flowering.

Leonotis leonurus – wild dagga 111

PROMISING

IT IS MUCH RESPECTED FOR ITS AGE-OLD
EDICINAL USES. ONGOING RESEARCH INTO
ITS PROPERTIES HOPES TO ANSWER
A FUNDAMENTAL QUESTION:
DOES IT REALLY CURE CANCER?

SUTHERLANDIA

LESSERTIA FRUTESCENS – SUTHERLANDIA

NAME

Lessertia is derived from the name of a French owner of an important private herbarium, J.P. de Lessert. *Frutescens* means 'bushy' in Latin.

Few plants have so many descriptive common names as the *Lessertia*.

Apart from sutherlandia, this bush is also known as the cancer bush due to its reputation as a cure for cancer.

Other common names like *klapper* (Afrikaans for 'rattle') refer to the sound of the rattling seeds in the dry pods, while bladder-pea and balloon-pea allude to the inflated fruits that resemble bladders. The lovely descriptive Afrikaans name *hoenderbelletjie* alludes to the red flowers that look like the *belletjies* or 'wattles' of a *hoender* or 'chicken'. *Eendjies* and *gansies* (Afrikaans for 'ducks' and 'geese' respectively) are the names given to the inflated fruits used by children as toys.

The most inspiring name, though, is *unwele* ('hair' in Zulu), which stems from the belief that sutherlandia stops people from 'pulling out their hair' in distress.

IN THE GARDEN

Sutherlandia is a fast- and easy-growing shrub that is ideal for arid areas and waterwise gardens. Plant in groups in a mixed shrub border or in a rockery where they will be very showy.

HEALING

The Khoisan and Nama as well as the early settlers used sutherlandia for cleansing wounds, to treat fevers and as a remedy for many illnesses. Today it is considered a good general medicine and an immune system booster. It is said to be effective against cancer, to stimulate the appetite and to reduce mental stress.

DID YOU KNOW

❖ *L. frutescens* is a member of the pea family (*Fabaceae*), the second largest flowering-plant family. *Fabaceae* contains more than 600 genera and approximately 18 000 species worldwide.

❖ In southern Africa alone, this family is made up of 134 genera and at least 1 300 species.

GENERAL HEALTH

❖ Sutherlandia can be used as a dietary supplement; tablets are available from pharmacies.

DECORATION

❖ The papery, bladder-like pods are easy to dry and keep their colour as well as their shape. They make a lovely addition to dry flower arrangements.

EASY TO GROW

❖ Perennial – flowers in summer
❖ Waterwise – drought resistant – full sun
❖ Shrub grows to 1.5 m
❖ Propagated from seeds – self-seeder
❖ Likes any well-drained soil
❖ Tolerates wind and frost
❖ Good contrast foliage and temporary filler in mixed borders, rockeries and pots
❖ Use as a pioneer in a new garden
❖ Attracts sunbirds and butterflies

TIPS Soak seeds for four hours in lukewarm water to improve germination. Do not over-water plants.

Lessertia frutescens – sutherlandia 115

SECRET

You don't know whether it is a male or a female until the day it flowers and shows off with pure silver cones (female) or yellow pollen on the fruits (male).

SILVER TREE

LEUCADENDRON ARGENTEUM – SILVER TREE

NAME

Leucadendron is derived from the Greek *leukas* meaning 'white' and *dendron* meaning 'tree'. *Argenteum* is from the Latin for 'silver' (*argentum*) and refers to the tree's silvery leaves.

IN THE GARDEN

Silver trees are threatened by urban development, mountain fires and foreign invader plants. Give them enough space in your garden, and plant another one if the first is not successful, as this will contribute to the conservation of this very special tree.

AIRBORNE FRUIT

The silver tree relies on wind for dispersing its seeds instead of having to attract dispersers. Each fruit looks like a small nut and is equipped with a 'parachute'. This is the dried part of the old flower and comprises the seed, which is suspended by the style under the plumed outer part of the flower. Once the seed is dislodged by strong winds, it can travel a considerable distance thanks to its design.

DID YOU KNOW

- ❖ The hairs on the leaves of the silver tree move. If the air is moist, the hairs stand up to collect moisture and the tree loses its silver look and appears green. When the weather is dry or windy, the millions of hairs on the leaves flatten to help the plant retain moisture.

 TO SNACK

- ❖ Remove the hard little *doppies* (shells) of the seeds, then roast the seeds or eat them raw.
- ❖ The seeds are very tasty ingredients for salads and breads.

 DECORATION

- ❖ The flowers last about a week, and are excellent for floral arrangements.

 BOOKMARK

- ❖ The leaves retain their silver colour when dried and can also be painted.
- ❖ They make wonderful bookmarks when dried.

 CHALLENGING TO GROW – FRAGILE

- ❖ Perennial – flowers in spring
- ❖ Likes medium water – full sun
- ❖ Tree grows to 5 m
- ❖ Propagated from seed and cuttings
- ❖ Prefers moist, acidic soil
- ❖ Tolerates wind and frost
- ❖ Good accent plant

  TIPS It needs perfect drainage and constant air movement. Provide enough space when planting as the roots must not be disturbed. Right positioning is key.

VISION

PINCUSHIONS DON'T BURST OPEN.
THEY FIRST OPEN UP TO THE NORTH WHERE
MOST OF THE SUNLIGHT COMES FROM.

WOULD THEY TURN SOUTH
IN THE NORTHERN HEMISPHERE?

PINCUSHION

LEUCOSPERMUM CORDIFOLIUM – PINCUSHION

NAME

Leucospermum is derived from the Greek *leukas* meaning 'white' and *spermum* meaning 'seeded'. *Cordifolium* refers to the heart shape of the leaves.

IN THE GARDEN

Pincushions are fabulous garden shrubs. They are fast growing and will last for about 10 years. Each year (starting within three years from seed) the highly ornamental blooms will decorate the shrubs for up to eight weeks.

IN NATURE

In the early morning nectar flows in abundance, attracting a multitude of insects, which, in turn, attract sunbirds and the Cape sugarbird. Their breakfast consists of insects and a good serving of nectar. In this way the birds transfer pollen from one flower to another.

IN THE WORLD

Overseas visitors are often amazed to see flowers they recognise from flower arrangements in their own countries growing in the wild in South Africa. Nurseries worldwide produce vast quantities of hybrids and cultivars of the South African pincushion.

DID YOU KNOW

❖ The young leaves of *L. cordifolium* are covered with soft hairs, but are hairless when the plant is mature.

TO SNACK

❖ Remove the hard *doppies* (little shells) of the seeds, then roast the seeds or eat them raw.

❖ The seeds are very tasty ingredients for salads and breads.

DECORATION

❖ Long-lasting cut flowers

EASY TO GROW

❖ Perennial – flowers in spring

❖ Likes medium water – drought resistant – full sun

❖ Shrub grows to 2 m

❖ Propagated from fresh seed and cuttings

❖ Likes light, well-drained soil but also tolerates nutrient-poor, acidic soil

❖ Tolerates wind and light frost

❖ Likes temperate rainfall areas and regular breezes

❖ Use as a focal point or plant in groups

❖ Attracts birds

TIPS Soak seed in water with hydrogen peroxide and rub the coat off to improve germination. Do not disturb the roots. Pruning is not needed as the old flower heads fall off.

Leucospermum cordifolium – pincushion 123

Symbiosis

Did you know that pincushions flower in spring to suit the ants?

The seeds are mature in summer and thus released when the ants are most active and most likely to disperse them.

Overberg pincushion

Leucospermum oleifolium – Overberg pincushion

NAME

Leucospermum comes from the Greek *leukas* 'white' and *spermum* 'seeded'. *Oleifolium* refers to the leaves that look like those of the *Olea*, the olive tree.

IN THE GARDEN

This pincushion is a lovely, rewarding feature in any type of garden. It goes well with many other fynbos plants or it could be used as a centrepiece in a small garden. The plants are long-lived and bear many flowers.

The insectivorous sunbird and the Cape sugarbird pollinate the Overberg pincushion in exchange for nectar and insects. For the artist, they are welcome subjects since they do not flee at the sight of a human being.

TO SNACK

❖ Remove the hard little *doppies* (shells) of the seeds, then roast the seeds or eat them raw.

❖ The seeds make tasty ingredients for salads and breads.

DECORATION

❖ Excellent cut flowers in a mixed arrangement

EASY TO GROW

❖ Perennial – flowers in spring

❖ Likes medium water – drought resistant – full sun

❖ Shrub grows to 1.5 m

❖ Propagated from seed and cuttings

❖ Likes well-drained soil – compost is appreciated

❖ Tolerates wind and light frost

❖ Attracts birds

TIPS This shrub is particularly attractive when planted in the foreground with taller *Proteaceae* like *L. cordifolium* or *Protea neriifolia* in the background. It needs good air circulation. Soak seed in water with hydrogen peroxide and rub the coat off to improve germination. Do not disturb the roots once planted.

Leucospermum oleifolium – Overberg pincushion 127

Aroma

Butterflies and bees love wild mint
when it's in flower,
but mosquitoes hate it.

Rub it on your body and have plenty
on your stoep and in your bedroom
– and of course in your kitchen too!

WILD MINT

MENTHA LONGIFOLIA – WILD MINT

NAME

Mentha is Latin for 'mint' and *longifolia* refers to the long thin leaves.

IN THE GARDEN

This fast-growing aromatic herb has many uses, which makes it a worthwhile addition to the garden. It will, however, pop up just about anywhere its underground runners take it. As it loves water, placing it under a leaking tap can be a nice way of utilising otherwise lost drops.

COOKING WITH WILD MINT

An old-time favourite with its strong fragrance and taste, it is delicious in salads and a variety of other dishes.

HEALING

This much-loved medicinal plant is easy to harvest and grows in most parts of the country. It is used for many different ailments such as respiratory conditions, headaches, indigestion, fevers and urinary-tract infections.

DID YOU KNOW

❖ *M. longifolia* and *M. aquatica* are the only two mint species that are indigenous to South Africa.

INVIGORATING OR RELAXING TEA

❖ Instead of adding mint to water to make tea, mix the fresh mint leaves with Chinese gunpowder tea and add sugar to taste ... it's delicious. Drink immediately for a relaxing effect. If you need a stimulant, let it stand for a while, stir, reheat and drink.

WILD MINT SYRUP

2 cups (500 ml) sugar – 3 cups (750 ml) water – 1 cup (250 ml) chopped wild mint

❖ Add sugar to water – boil and bring down to simmer until it reaches the consistency of syrup – add chopped wild mint – remove from heat – mix.

❖ The syrup can be kept for six months in a jar in a cupboard. It goes well with Karoo lamb, and is delicious with desserts.

RESPIRATORY AILMENTS AND DIGESTION

❖ Drink the tea to help relieve respiratory ailments, stomach cramps, asthma, flatulence, indigestion and headaches.

SKIN CARE

❖ In traditional healing, it is used externally to help in the healing of wounds.

EASY TO GROW

❖ Perennial – flowers from summer till autumn
❖ Likes medium water – full sun – semi-shade
❖ Creeper grows to 1.5 m
❖ Propagated by division
❖ Likes moist, compost-rich soil
❖ Good for pots
❖ Attracts butterflies and bees
TIP Cut back often to stimulate new growth.

APPEAL

HOW CAN A PLANT POSSIBLY EMANATE
MUCH BEAUTY WHEN ALL THAT IT HAS TO
GROW ON IS NUTRIENT-POOR,
ACIDIC, SANDY SOIL?

MARSH PAGODA

MIMETES HIRTUS – MARSH PAGODA

NAME

Mimetes is derived from the Greek meaning 'to imitate', alluding to the close resemblance of the toothed leaves to those of some species of other genera, such as *Leucospermum*.

Another common name for this species is pineapple bush. This name describes the shape and appearance, at the tips of flowering branches, of the soft brown leaves that have no flowers in their axils.

IN THE GARDEN

The plant is pollinated by long-tailed sugarbirds, which are attracted by the brightly coloured bracts and styles with their promise of a bountiful supply of nectar.

SURVIVAL

When the nut-like seeds are released two to six months after flowering, they fall to the ground only to be dragged away in no time by ants, which relish the fleshy lump at the base of the nut as it is a rich source of food. Once the seeds are safely housed, the ants will consume the fleshy parts and leave the remaining seeds. Stored away, these will be protected from birds and rodents. When fire clears competing vegetation, its heat and moisture will stimulate the seeds to germinate.

M. cucullatus

M. cucullatus

DID YOU KNOW

❖ Marsh pagodas grow rapidly and may start flowering after a mere two years of growth.

DECORATION

❖ The marsh pagoda ranks among the most strikingly beautiful of proteas and is a prized cut flower.

CHALLENGING TO GROW

❖ Perennial – flowers in summer
❖ Likes lots of water – light shade
❖ Plant grows to 1.5 m
❖ Propagated from seed and cuttings
❖ Likes soil with high moisture and low nutrient content – free drainage
❖ Tolerates wind and light frost

TIPS Positioning is crucial. Plant next to *Chondropetalum tectorum* or *Elegia capensis* to benefit from their cooling shade. Do not disturb roots. Do not add compost to the soil.

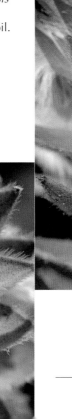

Mimetes hirtus – marsh pagoda 135

TWINKLE, TWINKLE

THE EXQUISITE BLUE STARS ARE A TRUE
DELIGHT IN LATE SUMMER WHEN
NOT MUCH ELSE IS IN FLOWER.

BLUE STAR

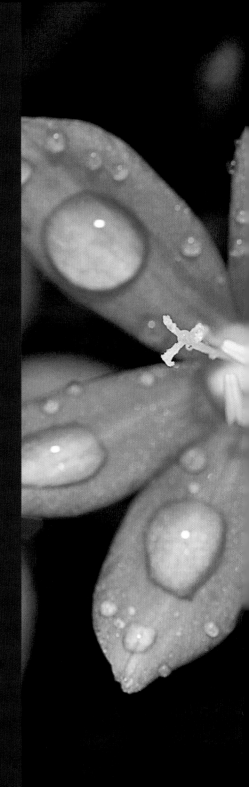

NIVENIA STOKOEI – BLUE STAR

NAME

Nivenia comes from the surname of James Niven, a gardener and plant collector. *Stokoei* is derived from the surname of the person who collected this species, T.P. Stokoe.

IN THE GARDEN

N. stokoei is on the list of rare and endangered species. Grow some in your garden and contribute to its conservation. Like other blue stars, it loves moist areas, especially during hot and dry summers, so if you have a fairly moist corner in your garden, give it to this delightful blue star.

IN NATURE

Nivenias grow close to water, along seeps and streams, or in crevices. The blue star occurs only in the Kogelberg Biosphere, a small stretch of wilderness in the Western Cape mountains near Cape Town.

 EASY TO GROW

❖ Perennial – flowers in late summer
❖ Likes medium water – semi-shade
❖ Shrub grows to 1.5 m in sheltered conditions and to 1 m in open areas
❖ Propagated from seed
❖ Likes well-drained, sandy soil
❖ Tolerates light frost
❖ Good for pots, beds and rockeries
❖ Used as accent plant
❖ Attracts bees and flies

TIPS Do not over-water in summer. Treat seeds with smoke to stimulate germination. Potted plants like seaweed fertiliser.

Nivenia stokoei – blue star 139

SACRED

Pharaohs worshipped the delicate blooms of the water lily that had the ability to rise pure and clean from slimy mud. The Egyptians compared them with purity and immortality – both yearnings of humankind.

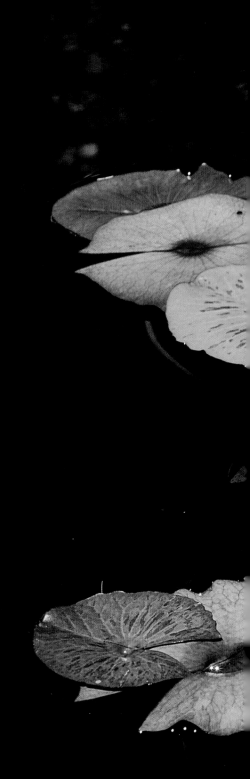

BLUE WATER LILY

NYMPHAEA NOUCHALI – BLUE WATER LILY

NAME

The genus *Nymphaea* is named after the Greek goddess of springs, Nymphe. *Nouchali* is named after one of the nymphs, Nouchal.

As the leaves provide resting places for frogs, the water lily is also called frog's pulpit or *paddapreekstoel*.

IN THE GARDEN

Blue water lilies are excellent plants for any respectable water garden. Their delicate fragrance adds to their much-praised beauty.

MYTHS

Water lilies usually grow in deep pools. Superstition has it that a *kaaiman* (merman) who dwells in these pools puts the flowers on the water to attract his victims and drown those who dare to swim, hence one of its common names, *kaaimanblom* (merman's flower).

A SNIPPET OF HISTORY

In ancient Egypt, the blue and white lotus was worshipped for thousands of years. The flower was depicted on monuments, in murals, on pottery and on furniture. Garlands were made of the petals and laid on the graves of pharaohs and priests. The flowers were in great demand for religious festivals, and also as gifts for visiting nobility as a gesture of friendship, or simply as food. It goes without saying that the lilies were widely cultivated. In China and Japan, too, the water lily is regarded as sacred and has long been cultivated.

COOKING WITH BLUE WATER LILIES

Also in South Africa, around the 1800s, the Cape Malay and farming communities in the Cape were quite fond of the lily's rootstock. It was eaten raw or in curries. In Namibia and Zimbabwe, blue water lilies are still on menus as a staple food.

? DID YOU KNOW

- ❖ *N. nouchali* is South Africa's most commonly grown indigenous water lily.
- ❖ Water lilies don't just float on the water, but are attached to roots in the soil.
- ❖ In traditional healing, a small dose of the flower tincture is used as an aphrodisiac or a stimulant, while a larger dose is given as an anaphrodisiac or a tranquiliser.

SUBSTITUTE FOR POTATO

- ❖ Cook or roast the tubers. They do not have a strong flavour though.

EASY TO GROW

- ❖ Perennial – flowers in summer
- ❖ Likes lots of water – full sun
- ❖ Aquatic plant grows to 30 cm
- ❖ Propagated by division
- ❖ Likes nutrient-rich soil with good, sieved garden loam or unwashed river sand as a base
- ❖ Tolerates light frost
- ❖ Good for ponds, water-filled pots, wooden barrels and old kitchen sinks
- ❖ Attracts frogs, bees and beetles

Nymphaea nouchali – blue water lily 143

TO BE OR NOT TO BE

NOT ALL THAT FLOATS IS A WATER LILY ...

FLOATING HEART

NYMPHOIDES INDICA – FLOATING HEART

NAME

Nymphoides is derived from *Nymphaea*, the genus of the water lily, which it resembles. *Indica* probably refers to its appearance in India. It is often called 'floating heart' because of its heart-shaped leaves.

IN THE GARDEN

Pretty and fast-growing, floating hearts are a delightful addition to ornamental ponds. They are an excellent indigenous alternative to exotic water plants and look best in combination with true water lilies.

SURVIVAL

If its water dries up, the plant will form roots at the nodes to help it survive.

DID YOU KNOW

- ❖ Floating hearts are not related to water lilies, although there are some similarities.
- ❖ Of all *Nymphoides*, *indica* is the only species found in South Africa.

EASY TO GROW

- ❖ Perennial – flowers in summer
- ❖ Likes lots of water – full sun
- ❖ Aquatic plant grows to 8 cm
- ❖ Propagated by division
- ❖ Likes moist soils
- ❖ Tolerates light frost
- ❖ Good for ponds and tubs

  TIP It is maintenance free, but must be kept under control.

Nymphoides indica – floating heart 147

MULTIPURPOSE

BIRDS LOVE THE WILD OLIVE, AS DO GAME
AND LIVESTOCK, AND PEOPLE FIND IT VERY
USEFUL IN MANY WAYS.

WILD OLIVE

OLEA EUROPAEA SSP. AFRICANA – WILD OLIVE

NAME

The Latin name for 'olive' is *olea*. *Europaea* means 'from Europe', and *africana* 'from Africa'.

IN THE GARDEN

Warthogs, baboons, mongooses and birds love the fruit of this wonderful shade tree. Cattle and game, however, prefer the leaves. The hardy wild olive tree is a blessing on farms in arid regions because it is an excellent fodder tree.

DECORATION

The wild olive yields beautiful, hard and heavy wood. It is used to make ornaments, fine, small furniture and fences.

HEALING

Traditional remedies prepared from this plant serve mainly to lower blood pressure and improve kidney function. The fruit of the wild olive was used by early Cape settlers to treat diarrhoea.

TEA

❖ The fruit is too small to eat, but the leaves could be used to make tea.

INTERNAL USES

❖ The leaf extract is traditionally used as a dietary supplement for the immune system.

❖ Decoctions of leaves are used for their diuretic and anti-diarrhoeal properties.

❖ Infusions of fresh bark are used to relieve colic.

EXTERNAL USE

❖ Infusions of leaves are administered as an eye lotion.

BONSAI

❖ Grow this wild olive as a bonsai.

INK

❖ Try making your own ink from the juice of the fruit.

EASY TO GROW

❖ Perennial – flowers in summer
❖ Waterwise – drought resistant – full sun
❖ Small tree grows to 3 m
❖ Propagated from seed – self-seeder
❖ Grows anywhere
❖ Tolerates wind and frost
❖ Good for gardens with difficult growing conditions
❖ Used as a screen and as a contrast tree
❖ Attracts birds and mongooses
    TIP Enriched soil will make this tree grow faster.

Olea europaea ssp. *africana* – wild olive 151

'CHIN-CHIN'

IN THE 1960S, YOU COULD SHIP
A BOX OF CHINCHERINCHEES
TO YOUR FRIENDS IN EUROPE.

ARRIVING THREE WEEKS LATER
IN PERFECT CONDITION, THE FLOWERS
WOULD OPEN AND STILL LAST
FOR ANOTHER SIX WEEKS!

CHINCHERINCHEE

ORNITHOGALUM THYRSOIDES – CHINCHERINCHEE

NAME

Ornithogalum is derived from the Greek *ornis* meaning 'bird' and *gala* meaning 'milk', and refers to the white flowers.

When the Romans regarded something as wonderful, they called it 'bird's milk'.

'Chincherinchee' is the English translation of the Afrikaans *tjienkerientjee*. It comes from the light high-pitched chink of the fresh stalks rubbing together. Both names were used in the eighteenth century.

IN THE GARDEN

Chincherinchees usually form large colonies and are very showy and, understandably, popular garden bulbs.

IN THE MARKET

Chincherinchees were introduced into gardens in Holland before 1700 and are known to have been cultivated in Europe since 1750. In South Africa, they are extensively cultivated in floriculture. From 1948 to 1968 you could buy locally grown cut flowers in Durban's city market. Today, KwaZulu-Natal relies on the Western Cape for its supplies.

DID YOU KNOW

- ❖ Chincherinchees are phototropic, meaning they bend in response to light.

TOXIC

- ❖ The above-ground parts of the plant can cause skin irritation and are toxic to livestock if ingested; baboons, however, seem to like them.

DYEING OF FLOWERS

- ❖ Place flower stalks of this showy bulb in food colouring to dye your flowers.
- ❖ The colourful flower heads are sold together with the authentic white flowers.

EASY TO GROW

- ❖ Perennial – flowers in late spring
- ❖ Likes lots of water – drought resistant – full sun or semi-shade
- ❖ Plant grows to 25 cm
- ❖ Propagated from seed and by division
- ❖ Likes well-drained, moist and fertile soil
- ❖ Tolerates wind and light frost
- ❖ Good for pots and gardens
  TIP They look best in groups.

FASCINATING

WHEN ALL ELSE GOES BROWN IN THE HEAT
OF SUMMER, THE DELICATE SEA ROSE
MAKES ITS GLOSSY APPEARANCE.

REMARKABLY TOUGH, IT GROWS EASILY NEAR
THE SEA, COPING WITH HARSH CONDITIONS.

SEA ROSE

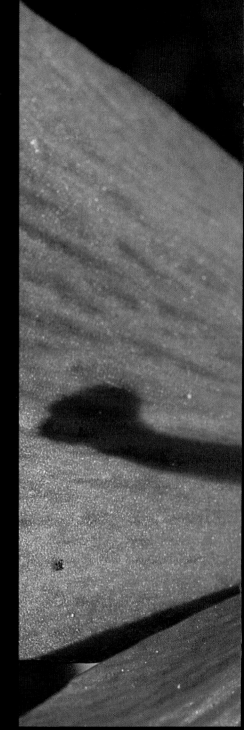

ORPHIUM FRUTESCENS – SEA ROSE

NAME

Orphium comes from the name *Orpheus* in Greek mythology, but there is no obvious link between the plant and the Greek poet. *Frutescens* means 'bushy' in Latin.

IN THE GARDEN

Sea roses are amazing. They grow easily near the sea, and have a remarkable ability to cope with wind, sand and slightly salty soil. They do well in a wet spot and will thrive once established. They will even withstand fairly heavy frost.

IN NATURE

Each fascinating flower has five glossy, but slightly sticky, petals. The bright-yellow twisted anthers in the centre are 'password protected' and respond to buzz pollination: when visited by a certain bee, whose wings vibrate at a particular frequency, the anthers open pores at their tips to release the pollen.

DID YOU KNOW

❖ *O. frutescens* is the only species in the genus.

DECORATION

❖ Sea roses make good, long-lasting cut flowers.

EASY TO GROW

❖ Perennial – flowers in summer
❖ Likes medium water – drought resistant – full sun
❖ Shrub grows to 60 cm
❖ Propagated from seed and cuttings
❖ Tolerates wet, sandy and brackish soil, and grows in any well-drained soil
❖ Tolerates wind and frost
❖ Good for coastal gardens, rockeries and watersides
❖ Attracts bees

TIPS Likes fertiliser. Place plants close to each other for support so that they don't fall over as they grow taller.

BOUNTIFUL

THE ABUNDANCE OF DELICATE PINK
AND YELLOW FLOWERS EMERGING FROM
HEART-SHAPED LEAVES IS NOT ONLY
DELIGHTFUL, BUT ALSO DELICIOUS.

SORREL

OXALIS PES-CAPRAE – SORREL

NAME

Oxalis comes from the Greek *oxis* meaning 'acid'; it refers to the sour-tasting sap of some species. *Pes-caprae* means 'looking like the foot of a goat' and comes from the Latin *pes* meaning 'foot-like part or organ' and *capraes* meaning 'of a goat'.

IN THE GARDEN

Sorrel is a hardy plant and grows in any soil, good or bad. It does well in full sun and complete shade but the flowers only open when it gets enough sunlight.

IN NATURE

Sorrel, with its pretty, brightly coloured flowers and clover-like leaves, is native to southern Africa and South America.

Sorrel spreads easily and can make meadows look deliciously attractive to sheep. Although the plant isn't generally considered poisonous, the consumption of excessive amounts of it can be toxic.

COOKING WITH SORREL

Sorrel is an example of tasty *veldkos* or 'bush food'. It is a well-known herb, found in many regions in southern Africa. It is much loved by the Nama children who will eagerly search for it in the shade of bushes, where the finest and tallest sorrel is found. The juicy roots can be savoured straight away, but at home they can be cooked with goat's milk to make a delicious porridge.

Oxalis purpurea

DID YOU KNOW?

- ❖ The seeds are explosively ejected.

COOKING

- ❖ Enjoy the leaves and roots as a snack.
- ❖ Add fresh leaves to salads, soups and stews.
- ❖ Grill or cook roots with milk and serve as a vegetable.
- ❖ *O. pes-caprae* is an essential ingredient of waterblommetjie stew.

HEALING

- ❖ *Oxalis* is used as a vermifuge and is good for treating scurvy, burns and abscesses.
- ❖ Use the leaves as a dressing.

EASY TO GROW

- ❖ Perennial – flowers in summer
- ❖ Likes medium water – drought resistant – full sun – semi-shade – full shade
- ❖ Dwarf plant grows up to 7 cm
- ❖ Propogated by corms and seed
- ❖ Likes any soil
- ❖ Tolerates wind and light frost
- ❖ Use as a seasonal ground cover

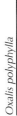

Oxalis polyphylla

Oxalis polyphylla

Oxalis luteola

Oxalis pes-caprae – sorrel 163

THE FLORISTS' GERANIUMS THAT ARE A FAVOURITE IN MANY WINDOW BOXES WORLDWIDE ARE ACTUALLY *PELARGONIUM* HYBRIDS FROM SOUTH AFRICA AND NOT OF EUROPEAN ORIGIN AS IS OFTEN THOUGHT.

HOODED-LEAF PELARGONIUM

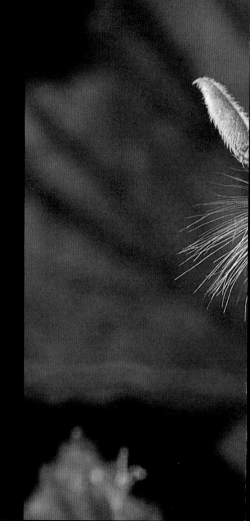

PELARGONIUM CUCULLATUM – HOODED-LEAF PELARGONIUM

NAME

Pelargonium is derived from the Greek *pelargos* meaning 'stork'. The shape of the *Pelargonium* fruit resembles the beak of a stork. *Cucullatum* comes from the Latin *cucullatus* meaning 'hooded' and refers to the shape of the cupped leaves.

IN THE GARDEN

It was in 1690 that the hooded-leaf pelargonium was introduced into England for cultivation. Easily grown and fairly adaptable, it is frequently visited by sunbirds, butterflies, long-beaked flies and moths.

DECORATION

In nineteenth-century Cape Town, the hooded-leaf pelargonium was used as an ornamental hedgerow.

HEALING

In traditional healing, diarrhoea, renal failure, fevers and colic are treated with *P. cucullatum*. The leaves are crushed to obtain drops of essential oils, which can be used for respiratory ailments.

DID YOU KNOW

- ❖ *P. cucullatum* is the parent of many modern pelargonium hybrids, including the regal pelargonium.

SKIN CARE

- ❖ To treat stings and abscesses, apply a poultice of fresh leaves.

DECORATION

- ❖ Cut flowers with branches will last for many weeks.

EASY TO GROW

- ❖ Perennial – flowers from spring till summer
- ❖ Likes medium water – drought resistant – full sun
- ❖ Shrub grows to 1 m
- ❖ Propagated from cuttings
- ❖ Likes well-drained, sandy soil
- ❖ Tolerates wind and light frost
- ❖ Good for pots, borders, rockeries and window boxes
- ❖ Attracts birds

Pelargonium cucullatum – hooded-leaf pelargonium 167

Velvet

A PEPPERMINT SCENT RISES
FROM THE SMOOTH HAIRS
ON THE LEAVES OF THIS SHRUB.

SOFT TO THE TOUCH AND PLEASING TO THE
EYE, THIS PELARGONIUM IS AT ITS BEST IN
THE EARLY MORNING WHILE STILL
COVERED WITH DEW.

PEPPERMINT-SCENTED PELARGONIUM

PELARGONIUM TOMENTOSUM – PEPPERMINT-SCENTED PELARGONIUM

NAME

Pelargonium is derived from the Greek *pelargos* meaning 'stork'. The shape of the *Pelargonium* fruit resembles the beak of a stork. *Tomentosum*, from the Latin, alludes to the thick leaves that are evenly covered with short, matted hairs.

IN THE GARDEN

The peppermint-scented pelargonium is an attractive garden plant. Choose a place in the garden where you can marvel at the sight of its velvety leaves covered with dew.

IN NATURE

Adapted to wind dispersal, the lightweight seed has a feathered tail which is coiled into a spiral. After the wind has blown the seed away and it has landed in suitably soft soil, the tail makes the seed twist around so that it drills into the soil like a corkscrew. This technique allows the seed to secure itself, until the first rains in autumn, when it germinates.

COOKING WITH THIS PELARGONIUM

The fragrant leaves of the peppermint-scented pelargonium make it a popular culinary herb.

COSMETICS

Pelargonium, more precisely *P. graveolens*, is cultivated on a large scale for its oil, which is a very important base in the perfume industry. It is widely cultivated in Japan, the Mediterranean, and now also in South Africa to supply the perfume industry in France.

DID YOU KNOW

❖ The glandular hairs produce the oil that gives the plant its marvellous smell.

FYNBOS ICE CREAM

1 litre milk – 1 litre cream – 8 rooibos tea bags – 500 g honey – 12 egg yolks – 100 g peppermint-scented pelargonium leaves (washed and finely chopped)

❖ Place milk, cream and rooibos tea bags in a saucepan and bring to the boil – squeeze tea bags and remove – mix honey and egg yolks until well blended – pour the hot rooibos mixture over eggs and mix well until slightly thickened – allow to cool down – when cool, add peppermint-scented pelargonium leaves – place in freezer – stir mixture every 20 minutes until frozen.

CULINARY FLAVOURING

❖ Add a few fresh leaves to flavour a jug of water.
❖ For added flavour, line your baking tin with fresh leaves before pouring in a chocolate cake mix.

EASY TO GROW

❖ Perennial – flowers in summer
❖ Likes medium water – drought resistant – semi-shade
❖ Plant grows to 50 cm
❖ Propagated from cuttings
❖ Likes moist, well-drained soil
❖ Good for embankments and pots
❖ Used as ground cover

TIP This plant loves seaweed-based fertiliser in spring and summer.

Pelargonium tomentosum – peppermint-scented pelargonium 171

Walking on Sunshine

Just as the sun replenishes our souls, the feathery bristles on the leaves of the featherhead capture the sunlight. In the early mornings and late afternoons it glows like magic.

FEATHERHEAD

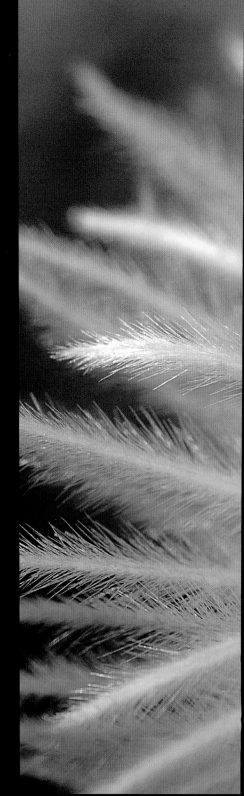

PHYLICA PUBESCENS – FEATHERHEAD

NAME

Pubescens refers to the short hairs on the leaves and stems of the plant.

The common name, featherhead, refers to the flowering tips that are surrounded by dense feathery bristles.

IN THE GARDEN

Featherheads flower in winter and it is not the flowers that attract attention, but rather the buff-coloured bracts that hold them.

The flowering heads are a favourite hunting ground for the yellowish crab spiders – their pale colouring is a good camouflage and hides them from the insects visiting the flowers.

A SNIPPET OF HISTORY

Between the seventeenth and eighteenth centuries, the strikingly beautiful *P. pubescens* and the similarly attractive *P. plumosa* were grown in European gardens. *P. plumosa* was one of the first dried flowers to reach Europe from the Cape.

DECORATION

- ❖ Looks good in posies and flower arrangements
- ❖ Long-lasting fresh cut flower
- ❖ Dries very well

EASY TO GROW

- ❖ Perennial – flowers in winter and autumn
- ❖ Waterwise – drought resistant – full sun
- ❖ Shrub grows to 1 m
- ❖ Propagated from seed
- ❖ Likes well-drained, acidic, sandy soil
- ❖ Likes winter rainfall areas
- ❖ Tolerates wind and light frost
- ❖ Good for pots
- ❖ Used as a filler plant
- ❖ Attracts bees, flies, beetles and crab spiders

  TIP Place the plants where early morning and/or late afternoon sunshine form a backlight so that the plant can be seen at its best.

Phylica pubescens – featherhead 175

VERSATILE

D YOU KNOW THAT THE PROTEA FAMILY
WAS NAMED AFTER THE PROPHETIC
SEA GOD PROTEUS, WHO WAS ABLE
TO TAKE ANY SHAPE HE WISHED?

THE PROTEA FAMILY

PROTEACEAE – THE PROTEA FAMILY

NAME

The protea family was named after the sea god Proteus in Greek mythology, who was the prophetic old man of the sea and shepherd of the sea's flocks.

Proteus guarded the seals of Poseidon on the island of Pharos, near the mouth of the Nile, and was able to adopt any shape he wished.

He knew all things – past, present and future – but disliked sharing his knowledge. If you wanted to consult Proteus, you had to surprise him during his siesta and tie him up. Even when caught, he would try to escape by assuming all manner of shapes. If you managed to trap him, he would return to his original shape, give you the answer to your question and plunge back into the sea.

Menelaus desperately wanted to find out how to get home after the Trojan War, knowing that because he hadn't sacrificed enough to the gods, he would not have favourable winds to sail back from Egypt. Disguised

as a seal, he crept up close and grabbed Proteus, who immediately turned into a lion, a dragon, water and a tree.

But Menelaus didn't let go and eventually Proteus gave up and became himself again. When Menelaus asked him how to get home, Proteus told him, 'You'd better go back to Egypt and sacrifice more to the gods.'

The moral of the story? When you have an urgent question about your way in the world and you already know the answer but it fails to satisfy you, going to great lengths to find the answer will only bring you back to what you already know.

IN NATURE

There are about 360 species of protea in southern Africa. Of these, 330 are confined to the Cape Floral Kingdom.

Leucadendron coniferum

Protea speciosa

Protea repens

Protea eximia

Leucospermum bolusii

Leucadendron globosum

Proudly South African

Prized worldwide as a splendid cut flower and probably the best known protea, the king protea has been South Africa's national flower since 1976.

KING PROTEA

PROTEA CYNAROIDES – KING PROTEA

NAME

Cynaroides comes from the Latin *Cynara scolymus*, the globe artichoke, which the flower heads are thought to resemble.

IN THE GARDEN

The so-called 'flowers' of *P. cynaroides* are actually flower heads comprising a group of flowers in the centre that are surrounded by large colourful bracts, which are often mistaken for the petals of a single flower.

On average, tall and vigorous king proteas produce between 6 and 10 flower heads per season, but some bear up to 40 per plant.

SURVIVAL

The king protea grows in areas where natural fires occur every 10 to 30 years in soil that is very low in nutrients.

Having to produce nutrient-rich seeds in a nutrient-poor environment is clearly a challenge, resulting in only a limited number of quality seeds. Covered by hairs, the seeds will stay in the old flower head for at least a year until fire releases them and they are dispersed by rodents and birds. The plant itself will re-sprout after fire, thanks to its thick underground stem containing a series of dormant buds.

DECORATION

It is not surprising that the king protea is a cherished garden companion and valued cut flower. Its ability to grow in different climatic conditions with varying flowering times adds to its popularity in the export market, where the flowers are needed at different times of the year.

Now grown worldwide, in countries like New Zealand, Australia and Hawaii, South Africa's national pride is cultivated in highly respectable quantities.

DID YOU KNOW

❖ The flower heads range from 12 to 30 cm in diameter.

APRICOT AND KING PROTEA CHUTNEY

*1 kg fresh apricots – 4 onions – 5 leaves wild garlic – 25 ml oil
– 1.75 litres water – 250 ml vinegar – 1 cup (250 ml) sugar
– 15–20 g king protea seeds*

❖ Remove stones from apricots – chop apricots and onions in chunks
– sauté apricots and onions with leaves of wild garlic in oil – add
water and vinegar – add sugar – cook slowly for 15 minutes – add king
protea seeds (take the hairy bits off) – cook for another 10 minutes
– allow to cool.

DECORATION

❖ The flowers in the flower head stay open for weeks, making it
a wonderful cut flower.

EASY TO GROW

❖ Perennial – flowers in summer
❖ Likes medium water – drought resistant – full sun
❖ Shrub grows to 2 m
❖ Propagated from seed and cuttings
❖ Likes acidic, nutrient-poor soil
❖ Tolerates wind and light frost
❖ Can be potted
❖ Attracts scarab and protea beetles

Protea cynaroides – king protea 183

FRENCH CANCAN

A VELVETY TOUCH
WITH PARISIAN FLAIR – THE OLEANDER LEAF
PROTEA EMBODIES SENSUALITY
AND ELEGANCE.

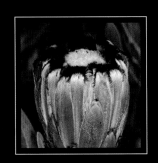

OLEANDER LEAF PROTEA

PROTEA NERIIFOLIA – OLEANDER LEAF PROTEA

NAME

Neriifolia means 'with leaves resembling those of the oleander' (*Nerium oleander*), which they do indeed.

IN THE GARDEN

In cultivation, the oleander leaf protea has a wider tolerance of soils than most other proteas. This ornamental shrub also produces lots of cut flowers, making it much sought after by gardeners.

A SNIPPET OF HISTORY

Keen horticulturists were growing *P. neriifolia* in glasshouses in Europe long before it was officially named in 1810. In fact, it was the very first protea to be mentioned in botanical literature, and from as early as the nineteenth century one could already buy cream or pink flowering plants from nurseries in England. It was also found in many a private collection.

SURVIVAL

The oleander leaf protea occurs among fire-prone vegetation. Adapted to survive the fires, it keeps its seeds safely in the old seed heads until, stimulated by fire and death, it opens up and releases the seeds. The natural summer fires are followed by winter rains, which provide the seedlings with much-needed moisture to grow strong enough to survive the upcoming summer heat.

DID YOU KNOW

❖ The hard leathery leaves protect the elegant oleander leaf protea against most insect attacks.

DECORATION

❖ Makes magnificent and long-lasting cut flowers

EASY TO GROW

❖ Perennial – flowers from autumn till winter
❖ Likes medium water – drought resistant – full sun
❖ Propagated from seed and cuttings
❖ Well adapted to various soil and climatic conditions
❖ Tolerates wind and light frost
❖ Attracts scarab and protea beetles, and birds

Protea neriifolia – oleander leaf protea 187

CANDY

Bountiful with sweet nectar, it was South Africa's national flower until 1976. The song *Suikerbossie ek wil jou hê* was composed on Lion's Head in Cape Town and shows how sweet the sugarbush must be to inspire such romance. The English version of the song became an international hit.

SUGARBUSH

PROTEA REPENS – SUGARBUSH

NAME

Repens means 'creeping', although this protea is anything but creeping. Its name was erroneously given, based on a misleading illustration. It is, in fact, erect and reaches a height of 2.5 m, sometimes even 4.5 m. Far more accurate is the common name 'sugarbush', honouring the species' reputation of producing more nectar than any other protea, to the extent that it sometimes overflows.

IN THE GARDEN

The sugarbush is undoubtedly one of the most reliable and easy-to-grow proteas. It is excellent for waterwise gardens, with *P. repens* ('Rubens') being the most desirable.

A SNIPPET OF HISTORY

P. repens was a first in many ways. In 1774, it was cultivated under glass in the Royal Collections at Kew Gardens where, in 1780, it became the first protea ever to bloom in cultivation away from the Cape. From 1890, it was also the first protea to grow outdoors in Australia, New Zealand and California in the US.

DECORATION

The sugarbush has been a good source of firewood for centuries. Today, the cut flower industry has produced many lovely hybrids, such as 'Sugar Daddy' and 'Venus'. Plants and attractive cut flowers are on offer in nurseries in New Zealand, Australia and Israel.

COOKING WITH SUGARBUSH

The early settlers used to make a syrup from the nectar that served as a sweetener.

DID YOU KNOW

❖ The process from closed to open flower takes six to eight weeks and the seed develops over the next seven months.

HOME-MADE SWEETENER

❖ Make your own home-made sweetener by shaking the flower heads into a bucket to collect the nectar, straining the nectar and boiling it down to a syrup.

HEALING

❖ This home-made sweetener is traditionally used as a cough syrup.

❖ Because of its low fructose content, the syrup is also traditionally used by diabetics.

EASY TO GROW

❖ Perennial – flowers in winter in the west and in summer in the east

❖ Waterwise – drought resistant – full sun

❖ Shrub grows to 4 m

❖ Propagated from seed and cuttings

❖ Likes any soil from heavy clay to deep white sand

❖ Tolerates wind and light frost

❖ Likes summer rainfall areas

❖ Attracts birds, bees, scarab and protea beetles

TIPS Soak the seeds in water (50°C) for 30 minutes before planting to stimulate germination. Needs a regular breeze.

UNIQUE

Proteoids and ericoids may be scarce in certain fynbos types – bulbs appear only in wetter months – but restios have the unique feature of being ever-present.

THE RESTIO FAMILY

RESTIONACEAE – THE RESTIO FAMILY

NAME

The word 'restio' comes from the Latin word *restis* and means 'rope'.

IN NATURE

Restios or Cape reeds take the place of grasses in fynbos.

What makes them remarkable is the fact that the solid green stems alone are responsible for photosynthesis, and not the small leaves, which are brown and papery.

South African restios are becoming very popular in many parts of the world, not only for thatching, but also as garden ornamentals and for ikebana.

Elegia stipu

Elegia filacea

Elegia persistens

Chondropetalum tectorum

Restio dispar

Ceratocaryum argenteum

Restios have the ability to grow in places that are not suitable for proteas or ericas. These are areas with low but predictable rainfall, where shallow-rooted herbaceous plants absorb all the moisture; or areas where the ground remains saturated with water for most of the year. Restios usually grow in autumn, spring and early summer. The best time to plant is at the beginning of the rainy season and the main requirements for happy restios are full sun, well-drained soil and lots of air movement.

TIP-TOP

RUB THIS SAGE BETWEEN YOUR FINGERS
AND SMELL THE STRONG SCENT THAT ARISES
FROM THE GLANDS ON ITS LEAVES. YOUR
FINGERS WILL BE STICKY; PUT THEM IN YOUR
MOUTH AND YOU WILL TASTE THE BITTER,
YET HEALTHY ESSENCE.

ROUGH BLUE SAGE

SALVIA CHAMELAEAGNEA – ROUGH BLUE SAGE

NAME

Salvia comes from the Latin *salvere*, meaning 'to be in good health', 'to cure' and 'to save'. *Chamelaea* in Latin means 'shrub'.

IN THE GARDEN

Sage enjoys a worldwide reputation as an excellent herb and is a beautiful plant, and the rough blue sage is no exception. What's more, the distinctive two-lipped flowers are cleverly designed for pollination: the bottom lip forms a platform for insects to land on while collecting nectar, and the hood of the flower hides the clever lever mechanism of the stamens. The anthers and stigma protrude just enough for the hinged anthers to move down to deposit their pollen and the curved stigma to collect pollen from the back of a visiting insect.

HEALING

Salvias, including *S. chamelaeagnea*, are extensively used in traditional medicine. Infusions are taken to treat coughs, colds, diarrhoea, colic, heartburn and flatulence.

COOKING WITH ROUGH BLUE SAGE

In Italy, sage is used as a garnish for pasta, fish and meat dishes, or vegetables. It can also be nibbled as an appetiser.

DID YOU KNOW

❖ Between 800 and 900 species of *Salvia* are found in the temperate and tropical regions of the world. Of these, 22 species occur naturally in southern Africa, mostly in the south-western Cape.

APPETISER: SALVIA À LA MILANESE

48 fresh sage leaves – 45 g flour – large lightly beaten egg yolk – 60 g breadcrumbs – 90 g clarified butter – pinch of salt (makes 8–10 servings)

❖ Wash and dry sage leaves – dip into flour and then egg yolk – coat with breadcrumbs – heat butter in a pan and brown leaves on both sides – remove from pan and drain on absorbent paper – salt lightly and serve.

GENERAL HEALTH

❖ Make tea from fresh or dried leaves and flowers. Sip slowly a few times a day.

EASY TO GROW

❖ Perennial – flowers in summer
❖ Likes medium water – drought resistant – full sun
❖ Shrublet grows to 1 m
❖ Propagated from seed and cuttings
❖ Likes well-drained, good garden soil
❖ Tolerates light frost and wind
❖ Good for rockeries and in beds
❖ Looks pretty next to blue agapanthus

TIPS The tips of the stems can be pinched to form bushy plants. Cutting back the shrub after flowering keeps it tidy and vigorous, and will make it last for several years in the garden.

Salvia chamelaeagnea – rough blue sage 199

WHOLESOME

The Zulu make good use of wild garlic.

Planted around the house,
it reputedly keeps snakes at bay.

WILD GARLIC

TULBAGHIA VIOLACEA – WILD GARLIC

NAME

Tulbaghia is derived from the name of an early governor of the Cape of Good Hope, Ryk Tulbagh. *Violacea* means 'violet-coloured'.

IN THE GARDEN

The popular wild garlic is useful for difficult hot corners of the garden, as it is quite drought resistant. Only two species are cultivated as ornamentals and enjoy popularity in cultivation.

Most of the species of *Tulbaghia* are adapted for moth pollination. Moths are attracted by the flowers' sweet nocturnal scent. However, *T. violacea* emits its scent during the day, attracting butterflies and bees.

COOKING WITH WILD GARLIC

The Zulu use both the leaves and the flowers to make a hot seasoning with meat and potatoes.

HEALING

Tulbaghia is a disinfectant. Traditionally, the bulb is used to treat coughs, colds and tuberculosis, and as a remedy for intestinal worms. Roots and leaves are widely used for the treatment of fever, asthma and constipation, whereas only the leaves are used to treat cancer of the oesophagus.

DID YOU KNOW

❖ The strong smell chases moles away from the garden.

❖ When crushed on the skin, the smell also keeps fleas, ticks and mosquitoes at bay.

WILD GARLIC SPRING ROLLS

60 g butter – 600 g cubed potatoes – 25 g wild garlic (chopped) – salt & ground black pepper – 8 sheets spring roll pastry – 1 beaten egg (makes 4 portions)

❖ Melt butter in a medium-sized frying pan over low heat – add potatoes and sauté over medium heat for 10 minutes – add wild garlic and cover pan for 5 minutes – remove lid and sauté until potatoes are done – add seasoning – allow mixture to cool – use 2 sheets of pastry per portion – place mixture on bottom half and roll up like a cigar – brush edge of pastry with beaten egg and fold edges in – refrigerate until ready to use.

SEASONING

❖ Use leaves and flowers in salads and other dishes.

COLDS AND COUGHS

❖ Boil freshly harvested bulbs in water to make a decoction and drink to relieve symptoms of colds and coughs.

CLEANSING

❖ The decoction is traditonally used as an enema as well as for washing the body.

EASY TO GROW

❖ Perennial – flowers in summer

❖ Likes medium water – drought resistant – full sun – semi-shade

❖ Plant grows to 40 cm

❖ Propagated from seed and by division

❖ Likes any well-drained soil

❖ Tolerates frost

❖ Good for difficult hot corners, edges, borders, rockeries and en masse for ground cover

❖ Used as a firebreak

❖ Attracts butterflies and bees

TIP Compost is greatly appreciated.

PYROMANIA

THE EXPLOSION OF PINK FLOWERS AFTER
A FIRE BRINGS ALONG A WEALTH OF SEEDS,
TO THE UTTER DELIGHT OF THE RODENTS
THAT FEED ON THEM.

NECTAR-FEEDING INSECTS ARE ATTRACTED
TO THE PINK WATSONIA, ADDING LIFE
TO THE BURNT LANDSCAPE.

PINK WATSONIA

WATSONIA BORBONICA – PINK WATSONIA

NAME

This plant is named after Sir William Watson, a London physician and naturalist. *Borbonica* means 'from the Ile de Bourbon' (now Réunion), as it was incorrectly thought to have originated from there.

IN THE GARDEN

At the crack of dawn, large bees visit the flowers of the pink watsonia, looking for sweet nectar in the freshly opened flowers. The styles of the flowers will, however, still be closed and will only unfold on the second day. At the same time the nectar levels rise. So, when the bees come back for the nectar, they will unwittingly pollinate the flowers by transferring previously collected pollen. By midday, the bees would have depleted most of the nectar – to the great disappointment of the sunbirds who will have to find 'sweeter pastures'.

DECORATION

- ❖ Watsonias flower for up to four or five weeks in the garden, but stay fresh for only a week or so in a vase.
- ❖ Dry watsonias look attractive with their purplish stems and seed capsules.

EASY TO GROW – LOW MAINTENANCE

- ❖ Perennial – flowers in summer
- ❖ Waterwise – full sun
- ❖ Plant grows to 1 m
- ❖ Propagated by corms and by division
- ❖ Likes well-drained soil
- ❖ Tolerates wind and light frost
- ❖ Likes winter rainfall
- ❖ Good en masse for borders, large pots and bedding
- ❖ Attracts birds, bees and flies

  TIPS Does best when kept well watered. Occasional fertiliser is appreciated.

Watsonia borbonica – pink watsonia 207

ALL-IN-ONE

WHAT LOOKS LIKE A FLOWER IS ACTUALLY
A SPATHE FORMING A CHALICE.

INSIDE, YOU WILL FIND A MULTITUDE OF
TINY MALE AND FEMALE FLOWERS,
ALL ARRANGED IN A SPIRAL ON THE SPADIX,
THE MALES ON TOP, THE FEMALES BELOW.

WHITE ARUM LILY

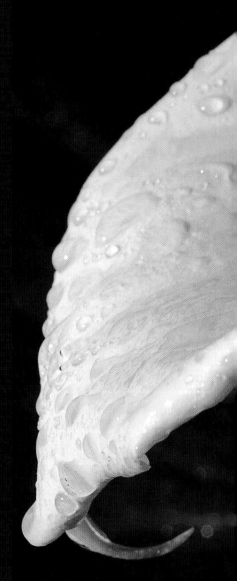

Zantedeschia aethiopica – white arum lily

NAME

This plant is most probably named after Professor Zantedeschi, an Italian physician and botanist. In classical times, the word *aethiopica* was used to refer to the regions 'south of the known world', i.e. south of Egypt and Libya.

IN THE GARDEN

The faintly scented flowers attract a multitude of crawling insects and bees, which will pollinate the flowers in exchange for food, each one in its own way. The white crab spider, for instance, visits the flower to eat the insects. It does not spin webs, but makes good use of its paleness as an effective camouflage in the spathe. The tiny arum lily frog also uses the arum as an easy ambush to catch unsuspecting insects.

Porcupines are crazy about the large rhizomes and will savagely destroy whole colonies of arum lilies. The good thing is that thanks to this brutal pruning, the plants regenerate fresher than ever with the most amazing flowers. It's worth the massacre!

HEALING

In traditional healing, the leaves of the white arum lily are used to relieve headaches. They can also be used as a poultice.

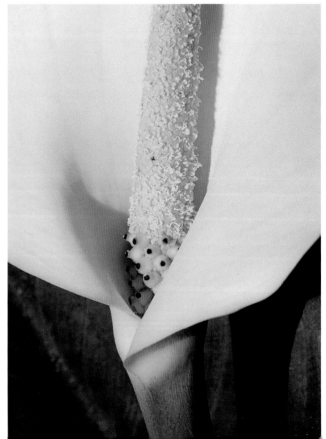

DID YOU KNOW

❖ The lush green leaves grow taller if the arum lily is planted in the shade.

TOXIC

❖ The arum lily is toxic and causes swelling of the throat when ingested.

SKIN CARE

❖ In traditional healing, the leaves are heated and applied as a plaster to wounds, boils and sores.

DECORATION

❖ The cut flower is long lasting.
❖ The white arum lily is a symbol of purity and is used for bridal bouquets.

EASY TO GROW

❖ Perennial – flowers from winter till summer
❖ Likes lots of water – drought resistant – full sun – semi-shade (if no permanent water)
❖ Plant grows to 1.5 m
❖ Propagated from seed and by division
❖ Likes rich, well-drained soil
❖ Tolerates wind and light frost
❖ Good along streams, edges and near ponds
❖ Used as a firebreak
❖ Attracts porcupines, crab spiders and frogs

TIPS Water abundantly during the growing season. Plant one near a tap as a screen.

Zantedeschia aethiopica – white arum lily 211

GLOSSARY

- ❖ *bakkie:* pick-up truck with an open back
- ❖ *decoction:* the liquor resulting from concentrating the essence of a substance by heating or boiling
- ❖ *doppie:* Afrikaans word meaning 'little shell'
- ❖ *dorpie:* Afrikaans for 'little town'
- ❖ *fynbos:* literally 'fine bush', an Afrikaans word used to describe the indigenous plants of the Cape Floral Kingdom
- ❖ *Khoikhoi:* original inhabitants of the Cape, nomadic herders
- ❖ *Khoisan:* a collective term used to refer to the San and the Khoikhoi, the original inhabitants of the Cape
- ❖ *kloof:* mountain gorge
- ❖ *konfyt:* Afrikaans for fruit preserves or jam with chunks of fruit in it
- ❖ *lekker:* Afrikaans word meaning 'enjoyable', 'pleasing' (informal)
- ❖ *Nama:* descendants of the Khoikhoi
- ❖ *sangoma:* traditional healer
- ❖ *sap:* Afrikaans word meaning 'juice'
- ❖ *trekboere:* Afrikaans word for 'migrant farmers'
- ❖ *veld:* uncultivated land or open countryside
- ❖ *veldkos:* food from the veld, including roots, berries and wild fruits
- ❖ *vygie:* Afrikaans word for 'fig'
- ❖ *waterblommetjie:* Afrikaans word for a fynbos plant used as a vegetable (literally 'little water flower')
- ❖ *witblits:* Afrikaans word for distilled alcoholic liquor, usually made from grapes (literally 'white lightning')

Index of common names

African daisy	24	protea family	176
April fool	100	pink watsonia	204
bitter aloe	20	red disa	64
blue star	140	restio family	192
blue water lily	144	rooibos	28
buchu	16	rough blue sage	196
candelabra flower	36	scarlet crassula	56
chincherinchee	152	sea rose	156
erica family	76	silver tree	116
everlasting	104	sorrel	160
featherhead	172	sour fig	44
fire heath	80	sugarbush	188
floating heart	144	sundew	68
flower of love	12	sutherlandia	112
honeybush tea	60	terracotta gazania	92
hooded-leaf pelargonium	164	thatching reed	48
horsetail reed	72	white arum lily	208
king protea	180	wild almond	32
kukumakranka	96	wild dagga	108
marsh pagoda	132	wild fennel	88
oleander leaf protea	184	wild garlic	200
Overberg pincushion	124	wild mint	128
peppermint-scented pelargonium	168	wild olive	148
pig's ear	52	wild pomegranate	40
pincushion	120	wild rosemary	84

INDEX OF PRACTICAL USES

HEALING

allergy	31
anti-inflammatory	14
asthma	103, 131, 202
babies	31, 86, 98, 99, 151, 166, 198
burns	23, 47, 163
cancer	114
chest pains	14
cough	110, 166, 191, 198, 202, 203
diabetes	62, 63, 107, 191
diarrhoea	31, 110, 150, 151, 166, 198
digestion	18, 19, 30, 31, 46, 47, 91, 98, 103, 130, 131
diuretic	18, 86, 90, 91, 103, 151
earache	47, 55
eyes	151
general	4, 15, 18, 19, 30, 31, 42, 46, 54, 55, 62, 63, 86, 90, 91, 98, 102, 103, 106, 110, 111, 112, 114,115, 118, 130, 131, 150, 151, 163, 166, 98, 199, 202, 203, 210, 211
hair	22, 30, 87
hangover	19, 31
homeopathic	18
hypertension	107
immune system	14, 31, 115, 151
laxative	22, 23
oral infections	15, 47
respiratory problems	14, 18, 62, 63, 86, 130, 131 135, 166, 203
Schweden bitters	22
skin	18, 22, 23, 30, 31, 46, 47, 54, 55, 99, 102, 106, 110, 114, 131, 163, 166, 210, 211
snake bite	110
toothache	47
tuberculosis	47, 202
vaginal thrush	47

RECIPES

chutney	183
drinks	19, 31, 63, 87, 91, 99, 107, 111, 131, 151, 155, 171, 199, 203
flavouring	18, 30, 86, 90, 91, 98, 108, 130, 163, 170, 171, 202, 203
ice cream	18, 31, 171
iced tea	31, 63
potato substitute	143
red Irish	31
salads	23, 47, 88, 90, 91, 119, 123, 127, 130, 163, 203
sauces	19, 31, 87, 90, 111, 131
snacks/appetisers	47, 91, 119, 123, 127, 163, 198, 199, 203
spring rolls	203
sweetener	190, 191
syrup	131, 135, 190

DECORATION

decoration	15, 19, 23, 31, 34, 39, 42, 43, 51, 67, 74, 75, 87, 95, 99, 107, 115, 119, 123, 127, 135, 150, 151, 154, 155, 159, 166, 167, 175, 182, 183, 187, 190, 194, 207, 211

COSMETICS

miscellaneous	18, 22, 30, 42, 66, 106, 170, 203

TOXIC

miscellaneous	14, 15, 35, 54, 55, 103, 155, 211

FURTHER READING & CONTACTS

This book is by no means comprehensive. If you have been inspired to explore some of the aspects in this book in more depth, the following sources may be of interest to you.

PUBLICATIONS

- Bean, A. & Johns, A. *Stellenbosch to Hermanus, South African wild flower guide 5*. Botanical Society of South Africa, Cape Town, 2005.
- Brown, N. & Duncan, G. *Grow fynbos plants*. Botanical Society of South Africa, Cape Town, 2006.
- Cowling, R., Richardson, D. & Paterson-Jones, C. *Fynbos, South Africa's unique floral kingdom*. Fernwood Press, Cape Town, 1995.
- Joffe, P. *Creative gardening with indigenous plants, a South African guide*. Briza, Pretoria, 2001.
- Joffe, P. *The gardener's guide to South African plants*. Tafelberg Publishers, Cape Town, 1993.
- Johns, A. & Johns, M. *Kogelberg biosphere reserve*. Struik, Cape Town, 2001.
- Johnson, D., Johnson, S. & Nichols, G. *Gardening with indigenous shrubs*. Struik, Cape Town, 2002.
- Kirsten, K. & Meyer-Faedda, L. *Gardening with Keith Kirsten*. Struik, Cape Town, 2001.
- Le Roux, A. & Wahl, Z. *Namaqualand, South African wild flower guide 1*. Botanical Society of South Africa, Cape Town, 2005.
- Manning, J. *Field guide to fynbos*. Struik, Cape Town, 2007.
- Pienaar, K. *What flower is that?* Struik, Cape Town, 1992.
- Pienaar, K. *Gardening with indigenous plants*. Struik, Cape Town, 1991.
- Rebelo, T. *Proteas – a field guide to the proteas of southern Africa*. Fernwood Press, Cape Town, 1995.
- Schumann, D. & Kirsten, G. *Ericas of South Africa*. Fernwood Press, Cape Town, 1992.
- Smith, G. *Gardening with succulents*. Struik, Cape Town, 2005.
- Van Jaarsveld, E., Van Wyk, B-E., Smith, G. & Bodley, E. *Succulents of South Africa*. Tafelberg, Cape Town, 2000.
- Van Rooyen, G., Steyn, H. & De Villiers, R. *Cederberg, South African wild flower guide 10*. Botanical Society of South Africa, Cape Town, 1999.
- Van Wyk, B-E. & Gericke, N. *People's plants*. Briza, Pretoria, 2000.
- Van Wyk, B-E., Van Oudtshoorn, B. & Gericke, N. *Medicinal plants of South Africa*. Briza, Pretoria, 1997.
- *Veld & Flora*. Botanical Society of South Africa, Cape Town (monthly publication).
- Visit www.plantzafrica.com for information.

Practical information

BOTANICAL GARDENS

- ❖ Free State National Botanical Garden – nursery, Danhof, phone (051) 436-3530.
- ❖ Harold Porter National Botanical Garden – nursery, Betty's Bay, phone (028) 272-9311.
- ❖ Karoo Desert National Botanical Garden – nursery, Van Riebeeck Park (Worcester), phone (023) 347-0785.
- ❖ Kirstenbosch National Botanical Garden – nursery and bookshop, Cape Town, phone (021) 799-8899.
- ❖ Lowveld National Botanical Garden – nursery, Nelspruit, phone (013) 752-5531.
- ❖ Natal National Botanical Garden – nursery, Pietermaritzburg, phone (033) 344-3585.
- ❖ Pretoria National Botanical Garden – nursery, Pretoria, phone (012) 804-3166.
- ❖ Walter Sisulu National Botanical Garden – nursery, Roodepoort, phone (011) 958-1750.

WEBSITE

www.InCelebrationOfFynbos.com

This website comprises a directory of nurseries, useful contacts and links, as well as loads of interesting information.

WHERE CAN ONE BUY FYNBOS?

In any of the botanical gardens listed above. Kirstenbosch NBG in Cape Town probably has the greatest variety and sells most of the plants in this book.

In the Western Cape there are a growing number of specialised nurseries.

You will also find a number of seed sellers on the Internet – the South African Protea Producers & Exporters Assocation is one of them.

ACKNOWLEDGEMENTS

My thanks to the following people for sharing their passion and time with me, and for offering their valuable assistance to my research and Paul's photography:

- ❖ Prof. Wim Tijmens (Stellenbosch)
- ❖ Pakamani Xaba, Roseline October, Jane Forrester and Caroline Joubert (Harold Porter National Botanical Garden, Betty's Bay)
- ❖ Dr Matt Buys, Cherise Viljoen, Lizette Engelbrecht and Graham Duncan (Kirstenbosch National Botanical Garden, Cape Town)
- ❖ Mark and Amida Johns (Cape Nature, Kogelberg Nature Reserve, Kleinmond)
- ❖ Tessa Oliver (University of the Western Cape, Biodiversity and Conservation Biology)
- ❖ Zibele Blekiwe (Groot Winterhoek Nature Reserve)
- ❖ Guy Palmer (Assegaai Scientific Services, Stellenbosch)
- ❖ Chris Burlock (Kogelberg Biosphere, Kleinmond)

And special thanks to :

- ❖ Roberto de Carvalho, executive chef of the Twelve Apostles Hotel in Camps Bay, for sharing his culinary secrets with me
- ❖ Jill Atwell, Betty's Bay, for inviting me into her inspiring fynbos garden and showing me the little arum lily frog
- ❖ Mark Botha, De Pakhuys, Clanwilliam, for spending his spare time giving me insights into the cultivation of rooibos tea
- ❖ Erica Goldstone for her around-the-clock availability when I needed to bounce an idea off her
- ❖ Last but not least, my husband Paul, without whose inspiring photography this book would not even have had a beginning

BIOGRAPHIES

PETRA VANDECASTEELE

Petra is an inspirational writer born in Belgium and now living in South Africa. She started as a freelance travel writer for a European magazine in 1993 and has been a copywriter for corporate clients since 1998. Petra contributes regularly to various South African publications – she enjoys capturing the essence of her subject and creating an inspiring reading experience.

PAUL GODARD

Paul is a Belgian-born landscape photographer with a PhD in science. Photography has always been his first love. It soothes his soul, and he experiences immense joy through photographing landscapes and flowers. Paul's work has been exhibited in Brussels, Paris, Washington, Harare and Cape Town. He is the main photographer for the Kogelberg Biosphere website, contributes to Petra's features and goes on assignments for clients in tourism and conservation.

Petra and Paul have travelled extensively, and since 1998 have lived at the edge of the Kogelberg Biosphere in Gordon's Bay, near Cape Town. They have two South African-born children, Enya and James. On winter nights Petra and Paul leave their bedroom windows open to hear the mating calls of the frogs in the stream running down the mountain a few metres from the house. Just after the rain, or sometimes right in the middle of it, they take their children for a walk to marvel at the delicate fragrances released by the fynbos.

With 'In Celebration of Fynbos' Petra and Paul offer you a glimpse into a delightful world of colour, extravagant shapes and fascinating uses.

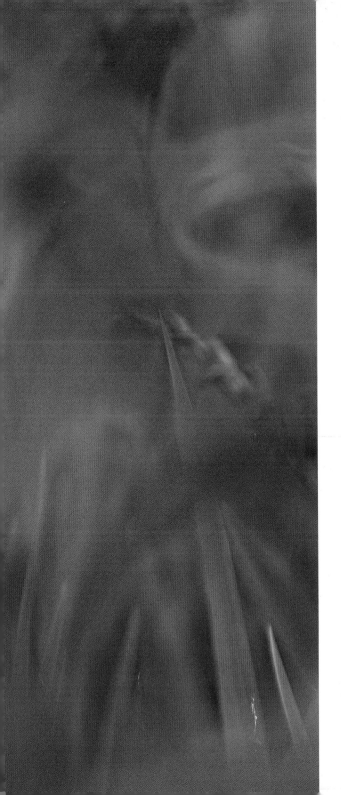

DISCLAIMER

The author and publisher have taken as much care as possible to ensure that the information contained in this book is as accurate as possible, but cannot make any expressed or implied representation of the accuracy, and cannot be held legally liable or responsible for any errors and omissions. All the advice contained in this book, medicinal and general, is intended for reference only and cannot replace the advice of a qualified physician. The author and publisher assume no liability for any consequences, loss, injury, misfortune or death resulting from using any plant described in this book.

Published by **Struik Publishers**
(a division of New Holland Publishing) (South Africa) (Pty) Ltd)
New Holland Publishing is a member of Johnnic Communications Ltd

London – Cape Town – Sydney – Auckland
Cornelis Struik House, 80 McKenzie Street, Cape Town 8001
www.struik.co.za

Publishing Manager: Felicity Nyikadzino Berold
Managing Editors: Lesley Hay-Whitton, Roelien Theron
Editor: Wendy Priilaid
Editorial Consultant: Cathy Patel
Cover Designer: Dr Paul Godard
Designer: Dr Paul Godard
Proofreader and Indexer: Hermanda Steele

Cover photograph: *Hermannia rudis*
Back cover photographs: from left to right
Erica masonii, Leonotis leonurus, Chondropetalum tectorum, Protea cynaroides

www.InCelebrationOfFynbos.com

Reproduction by Hirt & Carter Cape (Pty) Ltd
Printed and bound by Craft Print International Ltd

ISBN 978 1 77007 490 3

10 9 8 7 6 5 4 3 2 1

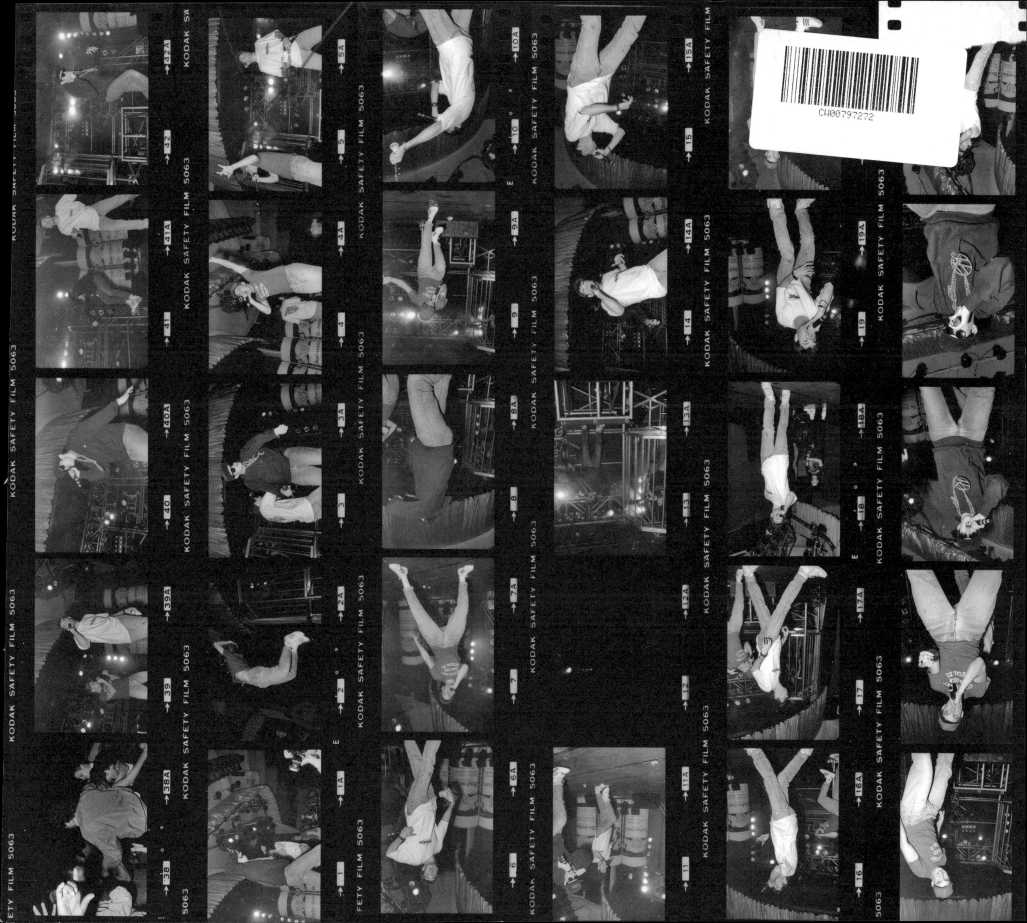

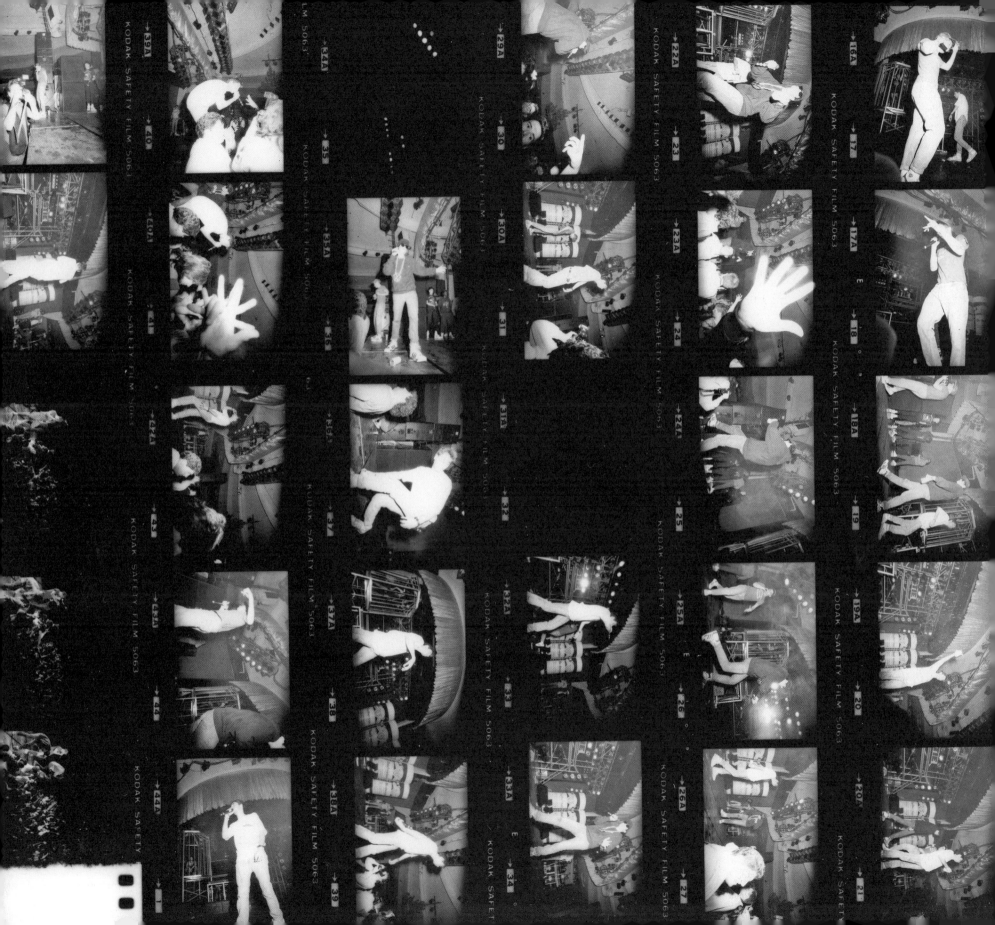

BEASTIE BOYS
BOOK DELUXE

THIS IS A CARLTON BOOK

Published by Carlton Books Ltd
20 Mortimer Street
London W1T 3JW

Text © 2014 Frank Owen
Design and layout © 2014 Carlton Books Ltd

ISBN 978-1-78097-271-8

Editorial Manager: Roland Hall
Design: James Pople
Production: Rachel Burgess
Picture Research: Steve Behan

A CIP catalogue for this book is available from the British Library

Printed in China

10 9 8 7 6 5 4 3 2 1

PREVIOUS PAGE: Beastie Boys bring the house down at the Montreux Rock Festival, Switzerland, 1987.

OPPOSITE PAGE: "The most ridiculous name we could think of," and internationally recognized logo, emblazoned on the stage, 1987.

OVERLEAF: The afterparty never ends; touring a successful debut album has its advantages, 1990.

SMASH and Grand Royal presents

BEASTIE BOYS

with special guest LEE "SCRATCH" PERRY

BEASTIE BOYS
BOOK DELUXE

FRANK OWEN

CARLTON
BOOKS

CONTENTS

— Introduction 8

100th St. Dropouts 12

Def Jam & 59 Chrystie Street 16

White Boy Stuff 18

Mike D 22

The Making of Licensed To Ill 26

No Sleep Till Brooklyn 30

The Big Break-Up 32

Paul's Boutique 36

The Making of *Paul's Boutique* 38

MCA 42

Boutique **Complete** 44

Paul's Boutique:
    Reception and Legacy 46

The Fallout from *Paul's Boutique* ... 48

The Making of *Check Your Head* 52

Grand Royal 58

Ill Communication 62

Ad-Rock 66

Musicians With Conscience 68

Root Down 72

Back in New York 76

Three Brothers 80

Coda: What Next? 86

— Skills to Pay the Bills: A Timeline ... 88

— Alright Hear This: Discography 90

— Index 94

— Credits 95

OPPOSITE: Ad-Rock sprays a Los Angeles concert audience with beer in February 1987.

ABOVE: Ad-Rock, Mike D, MCA, and DJ Hurricane attend the 29th Annual Grammy Awards,1987.

INTRODUCTION

I can still remember that cold winter's day in 1986 in London when I first clapped eyes on the Beastie Boys. I was penning a major story for *Melody Maker* about this new hip-hop record label called Def Jam out of New York City that was attracting major buzz on this side of the Atlantic. All week long, their British publicist had been feeding me stories about what bad boys the Beastie Boys were. The latest tale was that the hotel where the group was staying had just kicked them out for freebasing cocaine in their rooms. They were forced to move across town to a new hotel, a Holiday Inn in Chelsea.

So imagine my surprise when I walked through the door of the Beastie Boys' suite expecting to interview "the Sex Pistols of rap" only to see three skinny kids, none of whom was taller than five foot nine, and two of whom didn't look old enough to shave yet, let alone smoke crack. The one with the chubby hamster cheeks and the pimples on his face introduced himself as Mike D. "That's D as in Diamond," he said in a nasal New York accent. He was sporting a gold chain around his neck and a black leather hat on his head.

The person sitting next to him on the bed was Adam Horovitz (aka Ad-Rock), who was dressed in a plaid shirt and a blue baseball cap. Ad-Rock stood up and folded his arms high across his chest and tucked his hands under each armpit. He then tilted his head to one side and pouted. He looked like a child trying to imitate a rap video he'd seen on MTV. The third band member, Adam Yauch (aka MCA), sat in the corner curled up in a chair with his head bowed, his body partially covered by a leather jacket. He briefly looked up and gave me the stink eye. He then went back to pretending to be asleep.

After a brief discussion about why the British care more about their shoes than they do about their teeth (Mike D wanted to know where I got my "dope" cherry red Dr. Martens from), I flipped open my notebook and got down to business.

What were the Beastie Boys' major musical influences? "The Clash," said Mike D, and Ad-Rock agreed. The Beastie Boys used to be a hardcore band before they traded in their guitars for turntables and microphones. They counted The Clash, Bad Brains, and Black Flag as their major sources of musical inspiration.

"Hardcore and rap are identical," said Mike D. "The only difference is that rappers wear funny hats, and punks have funny haircuts." Then he added, "Except for peace punk homos like Dead Kennedys and Crass who are always going on about how fucked up things are as if people don't know that."

The Peace Punk Homos. What a great name for a hardcore band, I ventured. Wait a minute, wasn't one of the Beastie Boys' musical heroes Joe Strummer a "peace punk homo"?

"Nah, man," said Ad-Rock. "When I think of The Clash, I think of four homeboys drinking together. They're saying what's fucked up in their own lives not what's fucked up in other people's lives. The Clash weren't singing about politics."

Were we talking about the same band? The group that released a triple album called *Sandinista!* wasn't political?

Ad-Rock must have grown bored with the conversation because, without warning, he suddenly burst into rhyme: "Chilling on the corner with a 40 of OE/Me and MCA are friends with Mike D." Mike D, his cheeks puffed out like a Cabbage Patch Kid, provided the human beatbox accompaniment to Ad-Rock's rapping: boom-da-da-boom-boom-da-da-boom.

MCA roused himself from his funk when I brought up the touchy subject of what was it like being a white rap group in a musical genre dominated by African-Americans. He didn't see it as much of a problem. Skin color didn't matter when it came to music, he said, as long as the beats were "def." "The difference between you and us," he sneered, "is that we're into music and you're into politics." He spat out the word "politics" like it was a poison pill in his mouth.

How did they think the British public would react to their metal-rap fusion? Their debut album *Licensed to Ill* was due to be released by the end of the year.

"The way I figure it, England is going to get real ill by the end of the decade what with all this unemployment," said Mike D. "When you all get hooked on crack, that's when we're going to clean up. Or maybe we'll get hair extensions and an eye patch and get Boy George to fuck us. That way we'll probably be number one."

If there's an invisible line between being humorous and being retarded, then the Beastie Boys were about to cross it. It turned out all three of them were huge Benny Hill fans. The skirt-chasing British comedian had become a cult celebrity across the pond. "What we're trying to do with the Beastie Boys is cross Benny Hill with *The Young Ones*," said Ad-Rock. "So imagine the perfect Beastie Boys video. We'd have the girl from the David Lee Roth video with big tits and a big ass. We'd have her standing with a big bottle of Olde English [malt liquor] and then we'd smash the bottle in her face so we could steal her crack money."

It was fairly obvious from the get-go that someone was putting them up to talk like this, that they'd been trotted out in front of the British music press to create controversy to boost sales of their debut album *Licensed to Ill*. It was straight out of the Sex Pistols' cash-from-chaos playbook, and just like with the Pistols, it would backfire spectacularly, leaving the group to face the consequences, while the puppet-master pulling the strings got to skip away scot-free. In the Beastie Boys' case, their comeuppance came the following year after the album became a runaway success and after the *Daily Mirror* whipped up a moral frenzy about the band's behavior that resulted in a riot at a concert in Liverpool and Ad-Rock's arrest.

For now, however, the members of the Beastie Boys were willing to be part of a plan not of their making, playing the

ABOVE: A backstage pass for the infamous 'Together Forever' tour, with RUN DMC, 1987.

OPPOSITE: Serious trouble: the band pose for an early photoshoot, New York, 1987.

roles and speaking the lines that someone else had written for them: three arty downtown cool kids who had sprung from the bosom of Manhattan's bohemian elite, pretending to be suburban heavy metal meatheads.

"Have you heard about this thing called death metal?" chirped Mike D. "Slayer are death metal and they're going to be on Def Jam. They sing about it's raining blood and the priest is fucking a nun while he cuts a virgin's head off with a pickaxe. It's disgusting and Rick loves it."

Rick, I remember thinking, was probably the hairy dude with the shaggy beard who was now standing in the doorway of the hotel room. He looked like a roadie for Judas Priest. He was in fact hip-hop's answer to Malcolm McLaren. He introduced himself as Rick Rubin, Def Jam's founder and in-house producer. Like that other McLaren wannabe, Factory Records' Tony Wilson, he came with a manifesto in hand.

❝ What Def Jam does is syncopated rock beats... B-Boy breaks are all from rock records. ❞

RICK RUBIN

"Def Jam makes rock records for black people," Rubin said. "Before there were rap records, rappers used to rap over existing records and they didn't rap over soul records—they rapped over Aerosmith. That's why the Beastie Boys' potential for crossover is so great."

What Rubin was saying was nonsense. Hip-hop DJs didn't just cut up Aerosmith records for MCs to rap over. They snatched beats from a variety of sources: James Brown, Incredible Bongo Band, Chic, Funkadelic, even electronic music. Listen to Afrika Bambaataa's 1982 hit "Planet Rock" which featured Soulsonic Force rapping over Kraftwerk's "Trans-Europe Express."

"'Planet Rock' isn't hip-hop," Rubin claimed.

Afrika Bambaataa, the founder of the hip-hop fraternal organization known as the Almighty Zulu Nation, wasn't real rap music? That was news to me. "'Planet Rock' has a disco pulse beat," he explained. "That's electro. What Def Jam does is syncopated rock beats." Rubin began tapping on the table to show me the difference. "B-Boy breaks are all from rock records," he said.

Behind Rubin, the Beastie Boys nodded their heads in agreement; "Yeah, listen to Rick."

Before I left, Mike D asked me to deliver a message to a fellow writer who worked at a rival music paper who had trashed the Beastie Boys in the paper's pages. "Tell him he's a ball-slapping, dick-sucking homo," said Mike D.

"OK, but that's bit of a mouthful. How about I tell him you called him a 'peace punk homo'? That's easier to remember."

When I heard Licensed to Ill a few months later, I was stunned. Not just by the monolithic slabs of guitar and seismic drums— courtesy of Rick Rubin—that came crashing out of the speakers but also amazed by the Beastie Boys' rapping abilities; the witty interplay of the three voices swapping lyrics back and forth that were sly, clever, and often laugh-out-loud funny. Even the most jaded music consumer had to crack a smile at such lines as: "Man, living at home is such a drag/ Now your mom threw away your best porno mag" from "(You Gotta) Fight For Your Right (To Party!)".

You could certainly argue with some of the other lyrical content. On one song, "Paul Revere," Ad-Rock seems to be rapping about penetrating a young girl with a plastic bat: "The sheriff's after me for what I did to his daughter/I did it like this, I did it like that/I did it with a whiffle ball bat." What you couldn't argue anymore was that the Beastie Boys didn't have the skills to pay the bills. I was floored. Those three morons that I met at the Holiday Inn, they made this record?

Licensed to Ill—which took hip-hop out of the ghetto and introduced the musical genre to millions of teenagers around the world—was the Beastie Boys' original sin, a record they spent the rest of their career running away from or apologizing for. They'd sold their souls to Rick Rubin for a hit record and were ashamed of themselves.

Over the next quarter of a century, the Beastie Boys would continue to surprise and astonish, putting out seven more albums that explored with increasing sophistication a wide variety of musical genres, not just the hip-hop music the trio became famous for, but also jazz, funk, Latin music, and punk rock.

Who could have predicted that these callow youths, who sneered at the very idea of mixing music and politics, would within a decade become high-profile activists for Tibetan human rights? Who could have foreseen that Adam Yauch of all people would become the social conscience of the group and find contentment in later life as a Buddhist?

The Beastie Boys' music changed the world, but the trio also changed themselves. All three became better people but the transformation was most dramatic in Yauch. He spent the first half of his career acting like a juvenile jackass and after a spiritual awakening, spent the second half atoning for his jackassery by aspiring to be almost saint-like. MCA showed by example that a mature, thoughtful adult could still make gloriously riotous albums well into middle age. When he died from cancer in 2012 at the relatively young age of 47, the Beastie Boys had just been elevated to the Rock and Roll Hall of Fame.

Nobody could have predicted that.

LEGACY AND INFLUENCE

The death of Adam Yauch has left a big question mark over the Beastie Boys' future. Even if the remaining members—Mike Diamond and Adam Horovitz—never make another album, the group's legacy is secure. From the raucous rap-metal of their debut album Licensed to Ill to the back-to-basics punk-funk of Check Your Head and Ill Communication to the jazzy instrumentals of the last two albums, The Mix-Up and Hot Sauce Committee Part Two, the group has come to embody the idea of constant innovation and an attitude of uncompromising musical independence, proof positive that even in the age of American Idol, you can still sell tens of millions of albums by marching to your own beat.

The band's influence on other musicians runs deep. LL Cool J says that he owes his start as a rapper to the Beastie Boys because Ad-Rock discovered him and introduced LL Cool J to producer Rick Rubin. Eminem cites the group as a key factor in influencing him to become a rapper. Chuck D says he would not have achieved the success he did if the Beastie Boys had not picked Public Enemy to open for them on 1987's Licensed to Ill tour.

The musical trail blazed by the Beastie Boys paved the way for a slew of other bands, including Rage Against the Machine, Fall Out Boy, Korn, Sublime, Limp Bizkit, and Linkin Park.

Even Radiohead's Thom Yorke cites the Beastie Boys as a role model because of the group's artistic integrity. "We looked up to the Beastie Boys a lot when we were starting out and how they maintained artistic control making wicked records but still were on a major label, and the Tibetan Freedom Concerts they organized had a very big influence on me personally," he said in a statement released just after Adam Yauch's death.

Any rock or rap musician just starting out, who wants to make their own unique mark in the music world, would do well to look at the Beastie Boys' career to study a group that remained true to its roots while at the same time constantly looking for new musical ground to break, and who, with the notable exception of the debut album Licensed to Ill, maintained complete control over their own artistic identity. In the end, nearly as much as the music, the example they set for others to follow may be their greatest legacy.

What follows is a story about transformation and self-discovery, about friendship and loss, about the long road that three teenagers traveled to finally reach independence and maturity. It begins in a city that no longer exists: New York in the early 1980s, a crime-ridden hellhole to some, but to the Beastie Boys, a pop culture wonderland where vibrant new forms of music, art, and street fashion seemed to seep up through the cracks in the sidewalk.

OPPOSITE: Adam "MCA" Yauch gets a helping hand from the other Beasties in 1987.

100TH ST. DROPOUTS

Downtown Manhattan in the first half of the 1980s featured some of the meanest neighborhoods in America. Parts of the city looked like a giant archaeological dig. The abandoned buildings and burnt-out cars stood as testimony to a town that seemed as if it was regressing to a primitive past. Rats outnumbered the residents. Lunatics recently released from psychiatric hospitals wandered the streets. Crack vials crunched beneath your feet whenever you strolled down the disintegrating sidewalks.

It was a city where you could get mugged, or worse even, at nine in the morning by heroin junkies looking for their first fix of the day. Buying cocaine was easier than purchasing a carton of milk in some areas. Typical for the time was the handy acronym that people used to navigate their way around a notorious drug-infested nabe called Alphabet City: Avenue A, you're alright; Avenue B, be careful; Avenue C, you're crazy; Avenue D, you're dead. The city was broken, so shattered that many experts thought it was beyond repair.

Into this grim lunar landscape of decay stepped a new breed, casually antiracist, naturally postmodern (though they would have laughed at that term as ludicrously pretentious), who saw the city not as a dying institution but as one big adventure playground and who instinctively knew that punk and hip-hop were kindred musical spirits. They formed bands. They deejayed. They started record labels. They wrote their names on walls. They danced and skated in the street. They skipped across cultural and racial boundaries without giving them a second thought. They assembled from the bricolage of everyday life in this fading metropolis a sound and a style that would soon sweep the globe.

At the center of this cross-cultural fermentation were three Jewish kids from the city's more affluent neighborhoods:

ADAM HOROVITZ (born October 31, 1966) grew up in a three-bedroom apartment in New York's artsy Greenwich Village. His dad was the renowned playwright Israel Horovitz. His mom, Doris, was a painter and a free spirit, who encouraged her son to pursue music and acting to express himself. Adam's parents divorced when he was three and he went to live with his mother. Doris opened a store on W. 10th Street called Gee The Kids Need Clothes which sold secondhand clothes that she would refurbish with hippie slogans like "Keep On Truckin'" or "Peace." For his 12th birthday, Doris bought Adam an electric guitar—a Hondo II Professional—and a practice amp and, at 13, he performed in public for the first time at a talent show, where he played an

Elvis Costello song. He went to school at P.S.41 and screwed up a lot. He was always cutting class to smoke pot or play video games at the local arcade with his friends. At the age of 14, Adam was caught carrying pot in school but he didn't get into trouble with his teachers because Doris came to the school and explained it was her marijuana. He loved his mother. She was the coolest mom in the neighborhood. When he got into punk rock, she didn't freak out or lay a guilt trip on him like most parents would have done, but allowed his punker pals to crash in their apartment if they had nowhere else to stay.

MIKE DIAMOND (born November 20, 1965) grew up in a duplex apartment on Central Park West, one of the toniest addresses in the city, and attended Saint Ann's prep school, a posh private school in Brooklyn. His mother, Hester, was an

interior decorator and his father, Harold, sold museum quality twentieth-century art to a rich clientele. His family were assimilated Jews. When he asked his father what was their religion, he replied: "Capitalism." Mike was 13 when he heard The Clash for the first time. The first wave of punk had crashed and burned, but a second wave, a comically high-speed version of punk called hardcore, was all the rage in downtown rock clubs. He began sneaking into rock clubs like the Peppermint Lounge and CBGB's to watch bands such as Bad Brains and Black Flag. He shaved his head and wore multiple earrings in one ear. Before long, he got into writing graffiti. He and his friends would stay up all night tagging walls and then crash at his parents' pad—where original paintings by Picasso, Kandinsky, and Mondrian hung on the walls. He led a charmed existence but not one without tragedy. His father died in 1982, when Mike was 16.

ADAM YAUCH (born August 5, 1964) was an angry kid whose favorite hobby was blowing stuff up. He used the gunpowder from fireworks to construct homemade bombs, which he would detonate with an electronic trigger. The son of an architect father and social worker mother, he grew up in a big brownstone in Park Slope, a leafy Brooklyn neighborhood with a mixed Irish and Italian population. Rebellious by nature, he was 14 when he quit Quaker Friends School in Brooklyn, a nondenominational private school with a reputation for academic excellence, and enrolled in Edward R. Murrow, a much tougher public school in the Midwood section of Brooklyn. Yauch felt his parents were trying to shield him from the harsh realities of life in the big city by enrolling him at a private school. Hearing the Clash for the first time turned him into a punk rocker. Students at Edward R. Murrow spat on him in the hallway when he started turning up to school in combat boots and a trench coat with "White Riot" written on the back. Hearing "Rapper's Delight" by the Sugarhill Gang in 1979, while buying a slice of pizza made him want to be a rapper.

The Beastie Boys started out in the early 1980s as a hardcore punk band that poked fun at hardcore punk, more specifically poked fun at the suburban punks who had started to flood the downtown rock clubs as hardcore became more popular. The Beastie Boys were all cool urban kids so they naturally looked down their noses at kids from Long Island and New Jersey. The group, initially a quartet, consisted of Mike Diamond, who took care of the vocals because nobody else wanted to, Adam Yauch who played bass, drummer Kate Schellenbach, later a member of Luscious Jackson, and guitarist John Berry. It was Berry who introduced Yauch to Mike Diamond one night at the famous punk rock club CBGB's. The last member to join was Adam Horovitz, who replaced John Berry in January 1983 after Berry dropped out due to drug problems. Horovitz first spotted Yauch and Diamond at a Black Flag show.

"Beastie Boys" was a great name for the band not just because it was catchy and alliterative, but also because it succinctly summed up their jokey attitude. A group called the Beastie Boys was not an outfit that took itself too seriously. How the Beastie Boys got their name remains a bit of a mystery, though. According to Mike Diamond, Beastie is an acronym for Boys Entering Anarchistic Stages Toward Internal Excellence. Yeah, right. Another theory is that they got their name from the bass player of their favorite band, the Washington, D.C. hardcore outfit Bad Brains, who dealt marijuana in New York's East Village and would yell "Beast, Beast" if he saw the cops coming. Most likely, it was just something they came up with on the spot for a group they thought wouldn't last six months, let alone 30 years.

The group rehearsed at John Berry's loft on 100th St. in Brooklyn, and, as Adam Yauch would later recall, Berry's father would often come bursting in during their practices screaming, "Would you turn that fucking shit off already!" The band's first

gig was at the 100th St. loft to celebrate Yauch's 17th birthday in August 1981. Among the friends present was Dave Parsons, who owned Rat Cage, a dingy basement record store in New York's East Village. The Beastie Boys would often skip school to hang out there. Parsons told the band he was thinking of starting a record label and maybe they might want to put out a single on it.

The group's first paying gig was at punk club A7. Mike Diamond would later describe the experience: "It was like playing in your aunt's living room—that is if your aunt's living room had cat pee all over and was a part time crack house." Not long after they played the closing night of Max's Kansas City, the legendary New York nightclub-restaurant where a pre-Blondie Debbie Harry waited tables and where The Velvet Underground performed their last gig with Lou Reed, a concert immortalized on the seminal album *Live At Max's Kansas City*. Top of the bill that night was Bad Brains. The Beastie Boys struck up a lasting friendship with the members

of the Washington, D.C. hardcore outfit. The group admired the Beastie Boys for their ballsy attitude. When Mike Diamond formed a spin-off group called the Imperial Knights of Schism, he appeared onstage wearing black face paint with a mop on his head in imitation of Bad Brains, who were all Rastafarians.

After the Max's Kansas City gig the band broke up because, as Mike Diamond said, "It just wasn't funny anymore," but

reformed soon after when Dave Parsons asked them to record an EP for his new Rat Cage label.

There was little about the Beastie Boys' debut recording, the 1982 EP *Polly Wog Stew*, that would make the casual listener think that here was a major talent in the making. Except for the menacing psychedelia of "Jimi," which suggested that someone in the band was a secret fan of Public Image Ltd, the eight-song collection consisted mostly of the usual dime-a-dozen three-chord thrash-rock that six years after punk began sounded neither fresh nor convincing. "The cops have no respect for me/ The world is full of tyranny," screeched a 17-year-old Mike Diamond, who would soon enroll in Vassar, one of the snobbiest colleges in America. (To his credit, he did manage to get kicked out after one semester and was told never to come back.)

After recording the EP, the group disbanded, only to reform again when the EP came out. Then John Berry left and Adam Horovitz took over on guitar.

The early Beastie Boys shows were less musical events than a strange type of performance art. So it seemed appropriate that, in December 1983, with Adam Horovitz now a full-time member, the group opened for avant-garde noise rockers Sonic Youth at the East Village art space, the Kitchen, performing a cover version of Quiet Riot's "Cum on Feel the Noize" while wearing plaid deer-hunter vests and sporting caps with wool ear flaps. Call it the Elmer Fudd look.

"It was like playing in your aunt's living room—that is if your aunt's living room had cat pee all over and was a part time crack house." MIKE D

Sonic Youth's Thurston Moore recalled watching the Beastie Boys from the side of the stage, when he told *New York* magazine: "I remember Mike D looking out at the audience and saying, 'I don't know if we can keep playing, because everybody out here is old and has beards and you're sitting down.' He was really funny, and when he played, he was phenomenal. He was this rag doll of a singer; he would jump up and fall down on the stage, just like splat."

By this point the Beastie Boys realized that the group needed a new musical direction if it was to survive. Increasingly, they became fascinated by the booming hip-hop culture that was all around them in the streets. White punks were beginning to appreciate the musical revolution taking place just a subway ride away in Harlem and the Bronx, where black and Hispanic teenagers hooked up turntables to street lamps and scratched vinyl records to create a collage of blistering sounds, over which MCs improvised simple rhymes designed to keep the party moving. In 1982, a British expat named Ruza Blue, who managed punk impresario Malcolm

McLaren's New York boutique, invited Bronx native and Zulu Nation founder Afrika Bambaataa to play at The Roxy nightclub on 18th Street. The Roxy quickly turned into downtown's premier showcase for B-Boy culture in all its forms, from breakdancing and graffiti writing to deejaying and rapping.

Famous faces like Andy Warhol, Keith Haring, even David Bowie stopped by to check out this new scene. One of the less-famous faces in the crowd was Rick Rubin, a thickset guy with long dark brown hair and a straggly beard who looked like he should be fronting a satanic metal band. He was planning to start a small independent record label. He already had a name picked out: Def Jam. The Beastie Boys were also regulars at The Roxy, but it would be another year before they met Rubin.

In 1983, the Beastie Boys released the single "Cooky Puss," named after a cake sold at Carvel ice cream stores. "The idea behind the record," Mike D said, "was not to spoof rap but to spoof Malcolm McLaren ["Buffalo Girls"] and all those bullshit people who went to graffiti openings at art galleries." The group's first stab at a hip-hop record wasn't exactly bad, but at a time when Grand Master Flash and the Furious Five were redefining the boundaries of the genre with the groundbreaking social realism of "The Message", recording a crank phone call to an ice cream parlor, underpinning it with a fuzzy beat and then adding snippets from a Steve Martin comedy record, seemed, well, not exactly cutting-edge material. If Grandmaster Flash and the Furious Five was rap music's answer to Gil Scott-Heron, on the evidence of "Cooky Puss," the Beastie Boys were hip-hop's version of the Three Stooges.

"Cooky Puss" became a minor underground hit and caught the attention of Rick Rubin, who was getting ready to launch Def Jam out of his eighth-floor dorm room in Weinstein Hall at 5 University Place in Greenwich Village. A friend of the Beastie Boys knew Rubin. Rubin was this strange cat who fronted a hardcore band called Hose and who threw bikini parties in the basement of Weinstein Hall, where he deejayed next to a bubble machine.

"He has a bubble machine," exclaimed Horovitz, "that's fucking awesome." A man with a disco bubble machine was someone the Beastie Boys definitely wanted to meet.

LEFT: The Beastie Boys and producer Rick Rubin pose in kung-fu outfits in Washington Square Park, New York, 1984.

OPPOSITE: Not so clean-cut: the slightly older band goof around in front of the camera, 1987.

DEF JAM AND 59 CHRYSTIE STREET

After the Beastie Boys attended one of Rick Rubin's dorm parties, the trio bonded with the aspiring producer over their shared love of slapstick humor, pro-wrestling... and bubble machines. During these formative years, Rubin became particularly close with Horovitz, who often stayed overnight in Rubin's dorm room.

Rubin would later go on to produce a string of classic albums by everybody from Johnny Cash to Red Hot Chili Peppers to Adele, but at the time he was obsessed with the idea that the burgeoning hip-hop scene wasn't an outgrowth of dance music, as it was usually categorized, but a black version of punk rock. Both were simple and direct musical genres that could be played by teenagers with no musical experience. He saw a chance to mold the Beastie Boys into living proof of his theory.

Rubin encouraged the members of the group to start grabbing their crotches like real rappers did. Also like real rappers, all of them adopted alter egos. Mike Diamond became Mike D, Adam Yauch became MCA, and Adam Horovitz adopted the name King Ad-Rock. After pushing out Kate Schellenbach, the only female member of the band, Rubin became the fourth Beastie Boy, DJ Double R. The band started talking about "bitches," "faggots," and "hoes," stretching out the syllables in an exaggerated imitation of a ghetto accent. The trio—arty rich kids, two of whom went to posh private schools—had never talked like this before. Their liberal parents didn't raise them to disrespect women and gays. So where did they get it from?

"The sexism, the homophobia, that all seemed to arrive with Rick" said a key player who was close to the Beastie Boys during that period but who requested anonymity. "Look at their career before Rick arrived, there was none of that nonsense. Rick might have encouraged this not because he himself was sexist or homophobic but because of his twisted sense of humor. He probably thought it was hilarious."

Def Jam debuted in 1984 and the label's first release proved to be an out-of-the-box smash. "It's Yours" by T La Rock and Jazzy Jeff was a bare-bones hip-hop track that Rubin produced with Adam Horovitz using a Roland 808 drum machine. Rubin wanted to make a track similar to Run DMC's "Sucker MCs," only make it even sparser, even more stripped down. "It's Yours" signaled a more hardcore direction for hip-hop and became an underground classic that was sampled by many other rappers over the years, including Public Enemy, Nas, and the Beastie Boys themselves. Horovitz laid down some of the beats for the single but Rubin didn't credit him on the record when it came out—the

beginning of a pattern, the Beastie Boys would later claim. The buzz surrounding the record reached the ears of Russell Simmons, Run DMC's manager. Simmons was impressed, so impressed, he soon partnered with Rubin in his new venture.

Def Jam's second single "Rock Hard" featured the Beastie Boys freestyling over the AC/DC classic "Back in Black," underpinned by one of Rubin's trademark depth-charge beats: "Got real rock shit/You must admit/Not fake, not false, not counterfeit." The vocals were buried too deep in the mix, but you could clearly hear the basic outline of the formula that would soon make the Beastie Boys famous. Unfortunately, Rubin had failed to clear the sample and the single was withdrawn when AC/DC objected.

Around this time, Horovitz was sitting in Rubin's dorm room, idly rifling through a stack of demo tapes that Def Jam was inundated with after "It's Yours" became an underground hit. Horovitz wasn't expecting to find much but when he listened to a tape by a rapper from Queens, he was excited. The kid couldn't have been more than 15 but he rapped like Kool Moe Dee. Horovitz told Rubin to sign him, which Rubin did. The kid's stage name was LL Cool J. Rubin and Horovitz went into the studio with LL Cool J to record "I Need A Beat." While Horovitz received a production credit on the 12-inch release, his name was missing when LL Cool J's debut album *Radio* came out.

An unexpected windfall the next year—a $40,000 settlement from a lawsuit the group had brought against British Airways after the company had used a portion of "Beastie Revolution" (the B-side of "Cooky Puss") in one of their advertisements without the group's permission—allowed the group to move out of their parents' homes. The Beastie Boys rented their first apartment for $800 a month at 59 Chrystie Street in Chinatown. Above them was a sweatshop and below them a whorehouse called Club 59. The place was so infested with rats that the group bought BB guns to kill the rodents. The most striking feature was the black floor— the landlord or somebody had poured tar over the apartment's floor surface so it was like living in the middle of the road. Yauch's mother, Frances, was horrified at the living conditions. "I was afraid to even walk in the building," she told the *LA Times* in 1987. The trio immortalized the crash pad-cum-rehearsal space on "59 Chrystie Street" on their second album, *Paul's Boutique*. It was here that the Beastie Boys began to write the music for their debut album *Licensed to Ill*.

Adam Yauch liked to tell a humorous story about the $800 electricity bill the band received at the end of the first month when they were living at 59 Chrystie Street. The group asked their landlord why the bill was so high. They soon found out that Club 59 was tapping into their electricity supply because the Vietnamese pimp who ran the brothel was an illegal immigrant who couldn't get an account in his name with the electricity company. The pimp offered the services of his girls as recompense, but the band turned down his offer. So the pimp peeled off $800 from a wad of cash and handed it to them.

> ## " Their apartment was the worst thing you ever saw in your entire life. I was afraid to even walk in the building. ""
>
> Frances Yauch, on 59 Chrystie Street

WHITE BOY STUFF

When Rubin's new business partner, Russell Simmons, first clapped eyes on the Beastie Boys at the downtown nightclub Danceteria, he could barely believe his eyes. "They were wearing red shiny tracksuits and doo-rags on their heads," he said. "They came off as the worst type of blackface band. It was like they were making fun of black people."

Simmons was a hyperactive promoter and manager in his mid-20s from Hollis, Queens, who earned his nickname Rush because he talked so fast. Naturally gregarious with an infectious grin, Simmons was a born salesman. He started his career throwing hip-hop parties while still a student at New York's City College. The parties were so successful he dropped out of college to pursue a full-time career as a hip-hop manager. Russell's younger brother Joey Simmons often helped him hand out fliers for the parties. Russell encouraged Joey to form a hip-hop group, which he did. Joey became Run, the lead rapper of Run DMC.

In those days, hip-hop was a cottage industry, not the multimillion dollar business it is today. Most rap records came out on small independent labels that nearly always stiffed their artists. To get a record on the radio, you had to bribe a DJ. Forget about signing a hip-hop act through the black music department of a major label. Black music executives hated hip-hop.

Simmons saw the massive potential for growth that hip-hop had, especially among white teenagers if the music was presented to them in the right way. Three factors were holding hip-hop back from wider acceptance, Simmons believed. First, the way rappers presented themselves at the time: wearing space suits or go-go boots onstage looked silly to Simmons. He thought rappers should dress onstage as they did in everyday life, not like they'd just landed from another planet.

Second, the way producers recorded hip-hop was all wrong. Producers were always trying to make hip-hop sound more musical by adding unnecessary components such as synthesizers or disco horns. Simmons recommended the opposite approach: strip the music bare, just beats and rhymes, that's all you needed.

Third, the 12-inch single was regarded as hip-hop's natural medium, not albums. If a rapper had a big hit, he or she might then put out an LP, but it was usually 90 percent filler. Simmons believed that rappers should start thinking like rock musicians did—think of albums as coherent artistic statements, not just a collection of tracks stuffed together to make a quick buck.

If hip-hop did all this, Simmons said, rebellious white youths would flock to the music in droves, if only to piss off their parents.

Despite his reservations about the Beastie Boys, Simmons began to book the band as openers for more established rappers like Kurtis Blow and the Fat Boys. One night, the Beastie Boys piled into a white limousine and were driven over the East River,

deep into Queens, to perform at a ghetto club called Epic. The trio bounced onstage about three in the morning wearing doo-rags and matching Adidas warm-up suits. The angry looks on the faces of the crowd scared them. They looked like they wanted to kill the group and they might have if the turntables hadn't exploded, providing a convenient cover for the Beastie Boys to flee the scene.

After the show, Simmons took the shaken trio aside and tried to school them: a black audience will not accept white rappers acting black, he told them, because that's insulting, but they will accept white rappers rapping about white boy stuff because that's funny. The Beastie Boys heeded Simmons' advice and ditched the doo-rags and started dressing in jeans and sneakers.

Simmons saw an opportunity to introduce the Beastie Boys to a pop audience when, in 1985, Madonna's manager Freddie DeMann called looking to book Run DMC to open for the singer on her first major concert tour, The Virgin Tour. Simmons said: "Sure, $50,000 a night, but if you can't afford that, we have this other band called the Beastie Boys who will do it for $500 a night." DeMann accepted Russell's offer. The Beastie Boys didn't know Madonna personally, but Madonna had heard about the Beastie Boys at the nightclub Danceteria, where both Madonna and the Beastie Boys hung out.

Madonna's pop audience hated the Beastie Boys every bit as much as the ghetto audience. The trio would scamper around the stage like three crack-addicted monkeys, berate the audience with obscenities and give them the middle finger while grabbing their crotches, which left many of the Madonna wannabes—teenage girls dressed like their idol in fingerless lace gloves and crucifix earrings—so upset they would burst into tears. Parents who had accompanied their teenage daughters to the concert were furious at the Beastie Boys for upsetting their children. The group was booed offstage every night. Madonna's manager DeMann wanted to kick them off the tour. They were antagonizing the audience, making them angry on purpose, and this wasn't an angry crowd, not until

the Beastie Boys got onstage. Madonna insisted the trio stay on the bill. "They were so adorable," she would later recall. "I don't know why the crowd didn't like them." Adam Yauch reportedly got to have a make-out session with Madonna backstage.

Simmons continued to promote the Beastie Boys when he arranged for them to make a cameo appearance in the Warner Brothers movie *Krush Kroove*, appearing alongside performers such as Kurtis Blow, LL Cool J, the Fat Boys, and New Edition. The movie was a fictionalized account of the early days of Def Jam; the Beastie Boys performed a live version of "She's On It." Simmons recognized it was a historical inevitability that a white hip-hop act would one day take the music out of the ghetto and into the mainstream. Why not the Beastie Boys, he reasoned. Yet no one—not Simmons, not Rubin, nor Yauch, Diamond or Horovitz—could predict just how quickly the group would rise to the top of the charts.

ABOVE: Supporting Run DMC in concert was an important step in the Beasties being accepted by the wider hip-hop community, 1985.

OPPOSITE: The Beastie Boys and Rick Rubin bask in the New York sunshine outside Radio City Music Hall in 1985.

MIKE D

❝ We were depicted as larger-than-life villains, and by the time we got to Liverpool, England, people weren't there for the music. They were there because they were psyched to fuck shit up on a Saturday night, and the people we were working with could've steered us away from that but they didn't and only now can we look back and see that certain things had led us to that point. But you can't control it... life is way stranger than fiction. ❞ MIKE D

❝ We look at what we're doing as an inside joke. The fact that a larger audience gets it at all is a miraculous and happy thing. ❞ MIKE D

OPPOSITE: Fresh out of his teens, the newly born "Mike D" performs live and loud on stage in L.A., California—one of the first shows outside of New York City, 1987.

ABOVE, RIGHT: Mike D rocks the mic at a press conference in Montreux, Switzerland, 1987.

RIGHT: Mike D's infamous VW emblem chain sparked an international fad of "automotive jewelry theft" in the late 1980s, 1987.

LICENSED TO ILL

Their debut album, *Licensed to Ill*, released in 1986, was the first rap record to top the US *Billboard* charts and is still one of Columbia Records' fastest-selling debut albums to date.

1.	Rhymin' & Stealin'	4:08
2.	The New Style	4:36
3.	She's Crafty	3:35
4.	Posse In Effect	2:27
5.	Slow Ride	2:56
6.	Girls	2:14
7.	(You Gotta) Fight For Your Right (To Party!)	3:28
8.	No Sleep Till Brooklyn	4:07
9.	Paul Revere	3:41
10.	Hold It Now, Hit It	3:26
11.	Brass Monkey	2:37
12.	Slow And Low	3:38
13.	Time To Get Ill	3:37

OPPOSITE: Unexpected success with their debut album saw the Beasties take immediately to the road on their first world tour, 1986.

THE MAKING OF *LICENSED TO ILL*

In September 1985, Def Jam signed a $2 million distribution deal with Columbia Records. Def Jam now had a pipeline not just to a national audience but to an international audience. Columbia had decided to get into the hip-hop business after one of its top executives noticed how you couldn't walk anywhere in Manhattan in 1985 without seeing a kid with a boom box on his shoulder. Hip-hop was showing enough commercial potential that it made sense to partner with an independent label to exploit this new musical trend but which one? There were many. Def Jam was the obvious choice, especially now that *The Wall Street Journal* had just christened Russell Simmons "a mogul of rap."

Def Jam and Columbia celebrated the deal with a party on the rooftop at Danceteria. Rick Rubin ordered a thousand White Castle hamburgers for the guests and then encouraged the Beastie Boys to start a food fight while the video to the group's new single "She's On It" was beamed on to the side of a building. "She's On It" was the group's first video and showed the trio scampering along a beach while unsuccessfully trying to pick up a tall leggy blonde in a gold latex bikini. It clearly established the three personas as they would appear on their debut album—Mike D is the goofball, King Ad-Rock is the pretty boy, MCA is the surly tough guy—but it lacks the lyrical inventiveness they will soon be known for.

At the beginning of 1986, Rick Rubin cloistered himself with the Beastie Boys in Chung King Studios in Manhattan's Chinatown, to record the group's first full-length album, *Licensed to Ill*. The Beastie Boys wanted to call the collection *Don't Be A Faggot*, but executives at Columbia Records nixed that idea.

Rubin had already perfected his "less is more" production style the previous year when he produced LL Cool J's stark landmark debut album *Radio* at the same cramped production facility. The anti-Phil Spector, Rubin saw his role as a "reducer" not a "producer," someone who distilled the essential essence of hip-hop by editing out any unnecessary ornamentation.

Typically, Rubin would lay down a rumbling beat, often borrowed from Led Zeppelin's drummer John Bonham. Then he would add a touch of funk, say a lick from the Jimmy Castor Bunch or a snippet from a Trouble Funk record. Next he would snatch a crashing guitar riff, say something from Black Sabbath. Then it was time for the members of the Beastie Boys to do their thing. Freestyling lyrics about wiffle ball bats and Rice-A-Roni, rhyming Betty Crocker with Davy Jones locker, they boasted about smoking angel dust and snatching gold chains. They rapped about drinking beer and eating White Castle burgers. They name-checked the Smurf, the Popeye, and the

Jerry Lewis, then popular hip-hop dance moves. They related how they liked to toke pot laced with cocaine while watching television ("rolled up a wooly and watched *Colombo*"). They described taking revenge on high-school rivals ("went into your locker and smashed your glasses"). By the time they'd finished, there were more than 90 drug and alcohol references on the album, which must have been some sort of world record.

Of course, some of this was pure posturing. The Beastie Boys often rapped about being "dusted," being high on angel dust. It's unlikely that the group had ever smoked PCP. When asked about this in an early *Playboy* interview, Adam Yauch flat-out lied, claiming that dusted was "a reference to being unemployed." Similarly, it's highly unlikely that they had ever "pulled out their jammies" and shot people "in the mother-fucking face." It was a parody of rappers, some of whom had shot people and smoked angel dust in real life. The Beastie Boys were a hip-hop group sending up hip-hop, just as they used to be a hardcore group making fun of hardcore. However, as David St. Hubbins observed in the movie *This is Spinal Tap*, "It's such a fine line between stupid and clever" and that line would soon be erased, causing the group no end of problems that nearly led to the breakup of the Beastie Boys. That was the future, however, for now they had a tour to do.

Rubin stayed behind in the studio to finish off the final mix, while the Beastie Boys headed out on the road as the opening act on Run DMC's *Raising Hell* tour, which also featured LL Cool J and Whodini. As the tour progressed, Simmons could tell that black audiences were beginning to warm to the Beastie Boys now that they were being themselves and not trying to act black. They were rapping about skateboarding and whippets, not Cadillacs and gold chains. Instead of being booed offstage, they were being cheered, especially when the tour hit the Southern states, where they liked their hip-hop more danceable and lighthearted than in New York. The dopey white boy dance moves that made Horovitz,

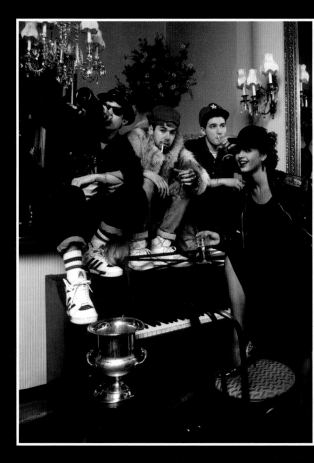

ABOVE: *Licensed to Ill* was about to redefine hip-hop music, and the bad boy antics and image of the group meant it would be impossible to ignore, 1986.

OPPOSITE: The first smell of success: photographer Sunny Bak captures the band in reflective pose, 1987.

The Beastie Boys are the most tasteless group in rock and roll, by their own admission. That is their act; that is what they sell. " BOB GUCCIONE, JR.

Yauch, and Diamond look like constipated crabs onstage drew laughter and applause from the audience. When they played the ultra-funky "Hold It Now, Hit It," the crowd would go wild.

"Russell did a lot to legitimize the Beastie Boys with the black audience when he put them on the Run DMC tour," says the author and former Def Jam publicist Bill Adler.

In July, Dr Dre (of *Yo! MTV Raps* fame), who was standing in for Rick Rubin as the Beastie Boys' DJ, quit the tour after the Beastie Boys left him stranded in a Miami hotel lobby. He was replaced by DJ Hurricane, one of Run DMC's bodyguards. Then

on August 16, 1986, the *Raising Hell* tour rolled into the 14,000-seat Long Beach Arena in California. The concert had barely begun when somebody threw a man over the balcony onto the stage.

Marauding gang members, especially a particularly violent faction known as the Insane Crips, started attacking the audience with knives and crudely fashioned weapons ripped from the seats. Despite the pleas for calm from the stage, fighting swept through the arena like a wildfire, overwhelming the security staff, some of whom were so scared of the gang-bangers they took off their shirts to avoid being identified. The Beastie Boys, who never got

to perform that night, were frightened enough that they and Run DMC barricaded themselves in their dressing rooms, fearing the gang violence was about to spill backstage. The police eventually stormed the arena in riot gear and managed to clear the venue. Luckily no one was killed—even the man who was thrown over the balcony survived—but 42 concertgoers were injured.

There were a handful of violent incidents earlier in the *Raising Hell* tour, but nothing like the scale of the mayhem in Long Beach. In the wake of the Long Beach debacle, venues across the country started to severely limit the number of rap shows they booked or to ban the music outright. The Beastie Boys found themselves being castigated by Tipper Gore of the Parents Music Resource Center on Oprah Winfrey's TV show for the lyrics of "Hold It Now, Hit It": "Head popping, body rocking, doing the do/Beer drinking, breath stinking, sniffing glue." *Spin* magazine's Bob Guccione Jr defended the group by saying: "The Beastie Boys are the most tasteless group in rock and roll, by their own admission. That is

their act; that is what they sell." Middle America was getting its first look at the Beastie Boys, and judging by the sour looks on the faces of Winfrey's audience, it hated them.

Any lingering perception that the Beastie Boys were simply a fly-by-night novelty act was dispelled with the November release of *Licensed to Ill*. "Three Idiots Make A Masterpiece" *Rolling Stone* headlined its review. *The Village Voice*'s Robert Christgau proclaimed: "The Beasties don't just thumb their noses at redeeming social importance —they pull out their jammies and shoot it in the cookie puss." *Melody Maker*, in the UK, crowned the release "Album of the Year."

If the ultra-funky "Hold It Now, Hit It" established their credibility among the hardcore hip-hop crowd, and "No Sleep Till Brooklyn," a play on the title of the 1981 Motörhead album *No Sleep 'til Hammersmith*, impressed the heavy metal fans, it was the insanely catchy "(You Got to) Fight For Your Right (To Party)" that turned the Beastie Boys into pop stars. It quickly became the national anthem of the frat boy nation and still, to this day, a rallying cry for teenage hedonists everywhere.

Columbia executives had pulled two songs from the album prior to its release, one called "Scenario" for being too violent and the other, a cover of the Beatles "I'm Down" because Michael Jackson, who owned the rights to the song, would not give his permission. Even the cover of *Licensed to Ill* proved controversial—an illustration of a plane crashing into the side of a mountain. American Airlines thought it looked too much like one of their aircraft and complained to CBS, Columbia Record's parent company. (Columbia was Def Jam's distribution arm.) The order came down from on high to pull the record and replace the cover; American Airlines was one of CBS TV's biggest advertisers. But Columbia Records executives refused. The sales of the album were out of this world. The album rocketed to the top of the US charts and the Beastie Boys became the first-ever hip-hop group to occupy the number one spot.

For Adam Horovitz, however, the success of *Licensed to Ill* was bittersweet. Just before the album's release, his mother, Doris, died after a long battle with alcoholism. The cover notes of *Licensed to Ill* dedicate the album to her.

LEFT: The Beasties' exuberant stage style, rock-sampled beats, and groundbreaking lyrics made them the most talked about group of 1987.

NO SLEEP TILL BROOKLYN

To support *Licensed to Ill*, Ad-Rock, Mike D, and MCA set out on their first headline tour. Rubin had just introduced the Beastie Boys to *Hammer of the Gods*, the seminal book by Stephen Davis that detailed Led Zeppelin's hard partying ways while on the road. The trio used the book as a blueprint for how new rock stars were supposed to behave on tour. Their riotous beer-soaked live shows featured go-go girls dancing in cages, giant inflatable beer cans, and a 20-foot-long hydraulic penis, an idea borrowed from the Rolling Stones. DJ Hurricane scratched records on top of a two-story-high six-pack of Budweiser. Mike D appeared onstage sporting a Volkswagen grille badge hanging around his neck. Fans of the group emulated the look and started to steal the badges from VW cars. There was even said to be a rider in their contract for condoms along with condiments in the dressing room.

If the shows were wild, the backstage antics were even wilder. They doused reporters with buckets of water, poured honey over groupies, trashed hotel rooms with abandon, and dumped soil in each other's beds. The band employed a "trim coordinator" who scoured the audience looking for cute girls to volunteer to go in the cage or to give backstage passes to. The Beastie Boys called them "blow job passes." Another employee's sole job was to throw beer to the Beastie Boys while onstage.

One of the most oft-repeated stories about the Beastie Boys on the *Licensed to Ill* tour is that the Holiday Inn hotel chain banned the boys after Ad-Rock cut a hole in the floor of his room as a passageway to MCA's room directly below. Mike D later admitted that the Beastie Boys had lied to reporters to bolster their image as crazy party animals. The story was a complete fabrication.

Other stories also failed to pass the smell test, such as the tale Yauch told *Playboy* about the groupie who wouldn't blow them unless they sang "Brass Monkey." Once they did, she got on her knees and blew all three.

From the outside, the members of the Beastie Boys seemed to be having the time of their young lives, acting out every adolescent male's fantasy, but behind the scenes Yauch, Diamond, and Horovitz were feeling increasingly trapped by the drunken frat-boy image that they and Rubin had manufactured. Mike Diamond worried that they were becoming the characters they had created. What started out as a joke wasn't funny anymore.

So when many Beastie Boys fans saw the *Animal House*-style antics in the video for "(You Gotta) Fight For Your Right (To Party!)," they didn't think, "That's cool, they're making fun of drunken frat boys," they thought, "That's cool, I should be more like them." How ironic that the same sort of meatheads who used to spit on them and call them names were now their biggest fans.

> **"Months on the road had frayed the bonds of friendship between the three. If they didn't get some time off soon, they were going to kill each other. "**

LEFT: Mike Diamond, wearing his now-iconic VW badge, poses with the other group members on a New York rooftop. Run DMC, who the Beasties initially supported in concert, can be seen in the background, 1987.

OPPOSITE: The Beastie Boys performing during their *Licensed to Ill* tour, accompanied by their infamous stage props, 1987.

MCA said the point was driven home when one fan approached him on the *Licensed to Ill* tour and said that he had smoked angel dust for the first time because he had heard the Beastie Boys rapping about it, and now he really liked it.

Months on the road had also frayed the bonds of friendship between the three. If they didn't get some time off soon, they were going to kill each other. Horovitz complained about not being able to see his new girlfriend, the actress Molly Ringwald, because he was constantly touring. He threatened to quit the group for good.

The British part of the tour that began in May 1987 was especially hellish. Unused to the British tabloid press, the band was flabbergasted to see a headline in the *Daily Mirror*, "Pop Idols Sneer At Kids With Cancer" when they arrived at Heathrow from Amsterdam. The report alleged that the Beastie Boys had caused a group of kids with cancer to burst into tears after they asked the band for autographs: "Go away you fucking cripples," the *Mirror* claimed the group had said. The Beastie Boys denied the story, but it hardly mattered whether it was true or not. The blood was already in the water.

Furious ministers stood up in Parliament and demanded that the Beastie Boys be kicked out of the country. The trio found themselves hounded by police and pursued by rabid tabloid journalists. Matters came to a head at Liverpool's Royal Court Theatre, when the Beastie Boys were forced off the stage only ten minutes into their set after being pelted with beer cans and bottles by the unruly audience. "We tamed the Beastie Boys," chanted the crowd, according to press reports of the time.

The next day in London, Adam Horovitz was arrested by the police and transported back to Liverpool to face questioning over the allegation that he had thrown a bottle out into the crowd, injuring a young woman. What had happened was that Ad-Rock had picked up a baseball bat and was swatting the missiles back into the crowd. A female fan was hit by a bottle. Ad-Rock was charged with assault, but later found not guilty. A few years later Molly Ringwald, Horovitz's then girlfriend, said it was Yauch who threw the bottle. Horovitz said nothing to the cops about Yauch's involvement to protect his buddy.

At last, the tour ended and the band flew home to New York. Time for some well-deserved rest and relaxation, but Russell Simmons had other ideas.

"They'd spent a whirlwind year on the road, surfing this wave of Beastie-mania and surviving the backlash, and ten minutes after they get back, Russell is asking them to make another album," says author Bill Adler. "And they're like: 'What the fuck. We're exhausted.'"

Instead of going back into the studio, the trio decided that they needed to spend some time apart before they drove each other crazy. They weren't sure they even wanted the Beastie Boys to continue. Horovitz moved to Los Angeles to be closer to Ringwald and to star alongside Donald Sutherland in the movie *Lost Angels*, as a troubled teenager sent to a psychiatric hospital. Yauch started a rock band called Brooklyn with the bassist from Bad Brains and the drummer from Murphy's Law. Mike D started a jazz group, The Flophouse Society Orchestra. In 1988, Yauch and Diamond left their beloved New York and joined Horovitz in Los Angeles.

THE BIG BREAK-UP

The discord between the Beastie Boys and Def Jam had only increased as the group became more successful. By this point, they refused to talk to Rick Rubin. The trouble began after *Licensed to Ill* was completed but before the album was released when Rubin tried to persuade Yauch and Horovitz to fire Diamond because Diamond wasn't "Beastie down." Yauch and Horovitz refused so Rubin approached Horovitz separately and tried to entice Horovitz to leave the Beastie Boys to go solo. Rubin thought that the group suffered from an imbalance of talent: the real star was Horovitz, while the other two were second-raters who were holding him back. Horovitz was offended and told Rubin that Diamond and Yauch were his friends.

The tension further increased on the set of the video for "No Sleep Till Brooklyn." Rubin wanted Slayer guitarist Kerry King in the video. He intended to use special effects to make King look 60 feet tall, while Yauch, Diamond, and Horovitz would scamper around the guitarist's feet looking like little elves. The group thought that Rubin was trying to hijack their video to promote Slayer, an act Rubin also produced.

Then Rubin planned to make a Beastie Boys movie called *Scared Shitless*, but the trio wanted to do their own movie on their own terms. The Beastie Boys went behind Rubin's back and met with Scott Rudin, the then head of Universal Studios, who offered them $4 million to make the picture. When Rubin heard about the meeting, he told the group that if they signed with Universal, he wouldn't allow them to perform their own music in the movie because Def Jam owned the rights. The Beastie Boys were forced to turn down the Universal deal.

"The problem with Russell and Rick is that they like to think that they're some sort of Svengali figures," Mike D confided in me at the time. "Historically, you get a figure like [Sex Pistols manager] Malcolm McLaren who takes credit for charting a course for the music. These people claim to have invented punk but when you actually talk to the musicians in the bands, you realize how full of shit these people really are."

The final insult came when the Beastie Boys tried to collect their royalties. *Licensed to Ill* had sold four million albums, so naturally the Beastie Boys were expecting a huge chunk of change from Def Jam. But when the time came to get paid, they were shocked to discover that Def Jam's coffers were empty. Columbia Records had frozen Def Jam's royalties after Jimmy Castor of the Jimmy Castor Bunch sued Def Jam and CBS for the unauthorized use of his song "Hey Leroy" on "Hold It Now, Hit It." There was money going out all the time, but no money

coming in. Def Jam was teetering on the edge of bankruptcy.

The band was furious. Their skills paid Def Jam's bills, but now there was no money left to pay them. They had received only a paltry $100,000 so far. Def Jam owed the Beastie Boys another $2 million dollars in royalties. Simmons said he was withholding the money until the Beastie Boys delivered the follow-up to *Licensed to Ill*, as they were contractually obliged to do.

"Fuck these guys," Yauch told Horovitz and Diamond. "We don't need Rick and Russell. We can do this on our own."

So the Beastie Boys officially announced their departure from Def Jam, vowing never to work with the label again. The group didn't speak to Rick Rubin again for more than a decade.

In the meantime, Rubin had also cut his ties with Def Jam. He had fallen out with Simmons over Def Jam's financial woes too. Rubin was the creative side of Def Jam; Simmons was supposed to take care of the money side.

A year after they relocated to Los Angeles, I phoned Mike D and read him a quote that his former manager Russell Simmons had just given me about the acrimonious split. "I dressed them, put them on a Madonna tour, put them on the Run DMC tour, put them in a movie, *Krush Groove*," Simmons said. "I gave them credibility in the black community and assembled a team that sold over four million records. I think it's a shame that they've forgotten what I've done for their careers."

Mike D laughed before replying: "Well, it's true. Russell would dress me, he would feed me, he'd bring me breakfast in bed each other morning—scrambled eggs and freshly squeezed orange juice with no pulp. He'd take my clothes to the laundry and wash my floors. He'd even change my diapers when they got shitty. That's why the Beastie Boys never used to have steady girlfriends; we had Russell."

Simmons' managerial smarts and Rubin's production skills played a huge role in boosting the Beastie Boys to the top of the charts. It's also true that the Beastie Boys played a bigger part in the production of *Licensed to Ill* than was commonly believed at the time of the album's release. The song "Hold It Now, Hit It"—the source of the Jimmy Castor lawsuit—was produced by the Beastie Boys alone without Rubin's help, the band later claimed. Russell Simmons admitted years later that the trio didn't get the artistic credit they deserved for producing parts of *Licensed to Ill.*

"It wasn't just about money," says Bill Adler a quarter of a century later. "It was about ego, inexperience, the massive level of success that neither the Beastie Boys nor Def Jam were prepared for. All these factors played a role in the breakup. Also, as Adam Horovitz now admits, Rick was the only one who was sober, everybody else was drunk all the time."

A bust-up was inevitable, says Adler: "Rick's influence on the Beasties was so massive, so monumental they had to leave him to flourish as creative artists. They needed to re-bond as a trio away from Rick just to show they could do it. They needed to salvage their sense of self-respect."

The Beastie Boys received some much-needed good news in 1988 when Capitol Records offered the band a lucrative $3 million dollar contract to make two albums for the label. Capitol was taking a big risk. The group was still technically under contract to Def Jam, even though the Beastie Boys' lawyers assured Capitol executives that the group was well within its rights to leave Def Jam because of their failure to pay royalties. Also, without Rick Rubin in their corner, who knew if the band could replicate the success of *Licensed to Ill.*

When Simmons heard about the Capitol Records deal, he instructed Def Jam lawyers to file a lawsuit against the Beastie Boys for breach of contract. "It's an old story," Simmons said at the time. "A major label comes in and steals an act from an independent after the indie has spent time, money, and imagination developing them."

" We don't need Rick and Russell. We can do this on our own. " MCA

1989

PAUL'S BOUTIQUE

A groundbreaking creative achievement, but a commercial failure,
***Paul's Boutique* has since become a critical highlight for the band**
and, in 2003, 14 years after its release, it ranked number 156 in
***Rolling Stone*'s prestigious *500 Greatest Albums of All Time*.**

1.	To All The Girls	1:29
2.	Shake Your Rump	3:19
3.	Johnny Ryall	3:00
4.	Egg Man	2:57
5.	High Plains Drifter	4:13
6.	The Sounds Of Science	3:11
7.	3-Minute Rule	3:39
8.	Hey Ladies	3:47
9.	5-Piece Chicken Dinner	0:23
10.	Looking Down The Barrel Of A Gun	3:28
11.	Car Thief	3:39
12.	What Comes Around	3:07
13.	Shadrach	4:07
14.	Ask For Janice	0:11
15.	B-Boy Bouillabaisse	12:33

OPPOSITE: Hungover and exhausted from the *Licensed to Ill* world
tour, the band head back to the studio to record the most important
album of their career, 1989.

PAUL'S BOUTIQUE, 1989

The Adam Horovitz, Mike Diamond, and Adam Yauch who turned up in the early summer of 1989 to attend the record release party to celebrate the group's second album *Paul's Boutique* didn't appear hugely different from the Def Jam-era Beastie Boys, except maybe mellower. In their drunken *Licensed to Ill* days, the Beasties would have started a food fight to disrupt a phony music biz stunt such as this one: the ceremonial raising of the Beastie Boys flag atop the landmark Capitol Records Building near Hollywood and Vine in Los Angeles. They looked good, considering all the drugs they were doing. Living in L.A. agreed with them. Mike D was sporting a red pimp hat straight out of Huggy Bear's wardrobe on *Starsky and Hutch*. Yauch was rocking a bearded beatnik look, and Horovitz looked like a movie star who had wandered into the wrong party. Three years on from *Licensed to Ill*, the Beastie Boys probably wouldn't trash your party anymore, but that didn't mean they had to pretend to like you.

Horovitz, Yauch, and Diamond sat together in a corner to engage in the traditional Beastie Boys sport of making life difficult for reporters. A woman from MTV was asking them what was the difference between *Paul's Boutique* and *Licensed to Ill*.

"One happened three years before the other, that's the difference," said Mike D.

"Do you see Rick Rubin: you both live in Los Angeles?" Diamond turned serious for a moment, his distaste for the group's former producer was obvious. Refusing to answer, he then smirked, "I heard Def Jam was auditioning new people to be the Beastie Boys."

"I heard Russell Simmons lost some weight, put on a cap, and is out there now busting rhymes," Horovitz also quipped.

As a Dixieland jazz band played in the background and an airplane wrote the name of the band in the hazy blue sky above, label president David Berman said a few words before the unfurling. He didn't sound like a man who was worried about losing his job. "The Beastie Boys are not a concept masterminded by someone else," he said, an obvious dig at Simmons and Rubin. "The extraordinary success of their album *Licensed to Ill* was no fluke. The boys have delivered what can honestly be described as the '*Sgt. Pepper*'s of Rap'." Berman was doing fine until he got to the next sentence: "The word on the street from respected rappers such as Eazy E and MC Hammer is that these guys are real indeed."

Members of the Beastie Boys entourage were taken aback. Did Berman just call MC Hammer a "respected rapper" and then compare him to the Beastie Boys? Some smart aleck started to chant: "Go Hammer. Go Hammer" as the Beastie Boys flag was being hoisted up the pole.

Notably absent from the party was the A&R man who had signed the Beastie Boys to Capitol Records, Tim Carr. The Beastie Boys had done a real number on this poor guy. He told

Berman after the album was delivered to Capitol that he needed to leave the country for a while, to relax and recuperate before he had a nervous breakdown. Sixteen months overseeing the progress of *Paul's Boutique*, begging, pleading, cajoling the Beastie Boys to stop screwing around and finish the album, had taken its toll. He was now incommunicado backpacking in the jungles of Thailand just as *Paul's Boutique* was about to hit the record stores.

Capitol Records publicists told the press how proud the label was to release such a masterpiece. *Paul's Boutique* was *Sgt. Pepper's Lonely Hearts Club Band* and the B-Boys were the Beatles of hip-hop—that was the official company line.

But, behind the scenes, Capitol's top brass were reportedly furious with the Beastie Boys. Who takes 16 months to make a rap record? It was unheard of. What the hell were they doing during that time? Goofing off, probably. The Beastie Boys seemed to delight in wasting Capitol's money, booking time at expensive recording studios, then playing ping-pong and air hockey instead of working on the album.

Sure, the critics would probably love it, but Capitol Records wasn't in the business of pleasing critics, but selling records. Where were the hit singles? Hit singles drive album sales, didn't the Beastie Boys know that? Not a single track on *Paul's Boutique* even came close to the obvious commercial appeal of "(You Gotta) Fight for Your Right (to Party!)". When pressed on this matter by Capitol staffers, what was the Beastie Boys reaction, other than to get on their high horses and claim they were artists unwilling to compromise their vision? Three years ago they were riding a giant dildo onstage and now they think they're frigging hip-hop Picassos. It was as if the Beastie Boys were deliberately trying to alienate the pop audience they'd attracted with *License to Ill*.

Another thing that was bugging the hell out of the suits at Capitol: the label had already spent $250,000 dollars clearing the sampled sounds on *Paul's Boutique*, but they weren't sure if they'd managed to catch everything. Exactly how many songs had been sampled: 100? 200? 300? The answer seemed to have been lost in the cloud of marijuana smoke that accompanied the recording of *Paul's Boutique*. What were they trying to do, set some sort of world record for copyright infringement? The possibility that Capitol Records would be hit with lawsuits well into the future because of the unlicensed use of other musicians' material only added to the apprehension surrounding the record's release at Capitol Records headquarters.

Now the publicity department was saying the band is refusing to sit down for any more interviews because they didn't want to be grilled by journalists about the breakup with Def Jam. Unbelievable. The Beastie Boys had managed to sucker one of the most storied record labels in the history of recorded music, the home of Frank Sinatra, the Beatles and Pink Floyd. No wonder Capitol Records had become the laughing stock of the music industry. If *Paul's Boutique* didn't sell, heads would roll. Backstage, the axes were already being sharpened. Number one on the hit list was label president David Berman, who had signed off on the Beastie Boys deal.

OPPOSITE: Spilling and swilling beer, Beastie Boy-style, 1990.

RIGHT: Respected rappers or frat-boy jokers? The band hit a creative high while making the difficult second album, 1990.

" Not a single track from *Paul's Boutique* came close to the obvious commercial appeal of '(You Gotta) Fight for Your Right (to Party!)'. "

THE MAKING OF *PAUL'S BOUTIQUE*

The rocky road that eventually led to the production of what many critics and fans regard as the Beastie Boys' most compelling work began a year and a half earlier in February 1988, when Yauch and Diamond jetted in to Los Angeles to take meetings with executives at a couple of major labels interested in snatching the Beastie Boys away from Def Jam. During the trip, Yauch, Horovitz, and Diamond went to the nightclub Enter The Dragon in West Hollywood and heard this densely layered instrumental track booming out of the speakers. Horovitz later told writer Dan LeRoi it was like "hearing four breakbeat records being played at the same time."

"That's incredible," Yauch said. "What is it?" The guy who ran the club, Matt Dike, told Yauch the track was called "Full Clout" and that he and two friends, E.Z. Mike (Mike Simpson) and King Gizmo (John King) had produced it. They called themselves collectively the Dust Brothers. Dike was a tall, friendly guy with a long face who had grown up in suburban New York but had adopted that irritating Californian habit of addressing everybody as "dude." He was the cofounder of the record label Delicious Vinyl, home to Tone Loc and Young MC. He was also a dude with a plan.

Dike lived in a cramped one-bedroom apartment on Santa Monica Boulevard in a seedy section of Hollywood. Somehow, he had managed to squeeze a makeshift eight-track recording studio into the living room area. The vocal booth was his closet, which he'd soundproofed with an old mattress. He knew that the Beastie Boys had fallen out with Rick Rubin so he figured they needed a new producer, and thought why not his friends the Dust Brothers. The Beastie Boys and the Dust Brothers could then record together at his studio.

The Beastie Boys had never heard of King or Simpson—few outside of the L.A. club scene had—but they were eager to hear more music. Yauch asked Matt Dike to send him a tape. The Dust Brothers Fed-Ex'ed the tape and waited to hear back. Simpson was excited. He'd been a Beastie Boys fan since the group's early singles. Two weeks later, Yauch called: "We're getting out of our deal at Def Jam, and we want to do a record with you guys. Book studio time for tomorrow, we want to start working."

The Beastie Boys had planned to produce their next album themselves or use different producers for different songs, but ditched that idea after hearing what the Dust Brothers had to offer. The Dust Brothers thought the music was too complicated for a hip-hop record and suggested they simplify the tracks to make them easier to rap over, but the Beasties told them not to

change anything. A reworked version of "Full Clout," retitled "Shake Your Rump," eventually appeared on *Paul's Boutique*.

"They had a bunch of music together, before we arrived to work with them," Yauch said in *Clash* magazine. "As a result, a lot of the tracks on *Paul's Boutique* come from songs they'd planned to release to clubs as instrumentals—'Shake Your Rump', for example. They'd put together some beats, basslines, and guitar lines, all these loops together, and they were quite surprised when

we said we wanted to rhyme on it, because they thought it was too dense. They offered to strip it down to just beats, but we wanted all of that stuff on there. I think half of the tracks were written when we got there, and the other half we wrote together."

Dike's plan had worked. The Beastie Boys and the Dust Brothers started to record together in his living room. The first tracks the Dust Brothers produced with the rap trio was the reworked version of "Full Clout"—the instrumental the Beastie Boys heard at the

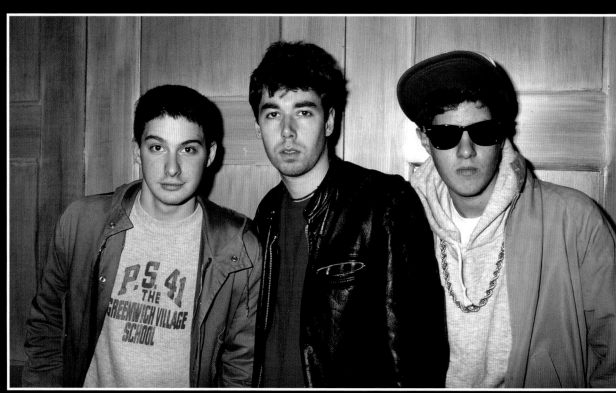

nightclub—and "Dust Joint," which later became "Car Thief" on *Paul's Boutique*. As it would turn out, every song on *Paul's Boutique* except one would be recorded at Dike's grotty little apartment.

The Beastie Boys took the demo tapes to Capitol Records' A&R man Tim Carr. Carr first saw the Beastie Boys perform in December 1983 at The Kitchen, a downtown New York art space where he worked. That was the same show where Diamond and Horovitz came onstage dressed like Elmer Fudd. Carr also had some experience in the hip-hop world managing rapper, artist, and MTV personality Fab 5 Freddy. But managing Freddy, as affable a chap as you could ever hope to meet, could not have prepared him for dealing with the Beastie Boys.

Carr wanted to sign them based on the evidence of the demo tapes but needed his boss, label president David Berman, to sign off on the deal, He, in turn, would need his boss, CEO Joe Smith, to agree to bringing the Beastie Boys on board. Smith was willing to meet with them, but he was highly skeptical. He had heard all the stories about the group's bad behavior. Hadn't they been banned from Columbia Records for stealing cameras or something? Also, the group was still signed to Def Jam. He didn't want to spend money on a record that might never see the light of day because of legal issues. Smith, an avid art collector, had no idea what a winsome young fellow Mike Diamond could be when he wasn't being a Beastie Boy.

"Mike walks into his office and he's like, 'You brought a Brach [Paul Brach, American abstract painter] from my father', Carr told author Dan LeRoy for LeRoy's book *Paul's Boutique* "and Joe Smith is like 'What.' And he realizes that this kid, who is this terror that he's been told about, is all of sudden the son of the most important art dealer in New York."

Smith changed his mind about the Beastie Boys. The deal went through and Capitol offered the Beastie Boys a deal worth reportedly a cool $3 million dollars. It was cash-from-chaos redux, the Great Rock & Roll Swindle, hip-hop style.

That was a big sum of money for 1988 and the Beastie Boys set about spending some of it. All three moved onto the top floor of the Le Mondrian, a luxury hotel on Sunset Boulevard with a giant mural that covered the nine-story exterior that paid tribute to Dutch abstract painter Piet Mondrian. The boutique hotel was only a ten-minute car ride from where Rick Rubin was living in a white Mediterranean-style villa in the Hollywood Hills. Rubin had also lived at Le Mondrian when he first moved to Los Angeles before he relocated to his current accommodation. Le Mondrian had a reputation as a hangout for rock stars from Keith Richards to Elton John, no doubt helped by its location proximate to the rock clubs on Sunset Strip. It was the perfect launch pad for three young rock stars new to the city, but with plenty of money to throw around, who wanted to have a really good time.

Instead of working on the album, the Beastie Boys threw themselves headlong into L.A.'s see-and-be-seen party scene. They spent their nights hanging out in nightclubs with Matt Dike and

OPPOSITE: The band prepare to mix it up in the studio for the recording of *Paul's Boutique*, 1988.

ABOVE LEFT: MCA in danger of a DUI, on his Suzuki moped, New York, 1988.

ABOVE RIGHT: Mike D attends a Christmas party, 1988.

RIGHT: The band shake their rumps live onstage, with DJ Hurricane, 1988.

their days sunning themselves by the pool or skiing in the mountains or dropping acid in the desert. They surrounded themselves with a new group of friends, the young Hollywood set: the sons and daughters of celebrities. Two people they became particularly close to were sister and brother, Ione Skye, the actress, and Donovan Leitch, later lead singer of Nancy Boy. Horovitz dated Ione Skye after he split up with Molly Ringwald. Skye had just left Anthony Kiedis from the Red Hot Chili Peppers. They also counted Karis Jagger, daughter of Mick Jagger, and Mick Fleetwood's daughter Amy Fleetwood among their friends. Yauch dated the drop-dead-gorgeous model and actress Lisa Ann Cabasa.

In the meantime, Horovitz had discovered a new hobby—crashing rental cars on purpose, which he rapped about on "High Plains Drifter" from *Paul's Boutique*: "I'm charming and dashing, I'm rental car bashing."

The Beastie Boys' idea of work was to wake themselves from their marijuana stupor and take the elevator back to their rooms just in time to throw eggs at the people lining up outside the famous Comedy Store across the street.

More hi-jinks ensued when process servers began turning up at Le Mondrian. The Def Jam lawsuit was heating up.

this, man, we've gotta make another record, otherwise how we gonna get into all these U2 parties?'!"

Joking aside, the group had been out of the spotlight for so long, over two years, an eternity in the fast-paced world of hip-hop. They needed to get back in the game. People were starting to forget about them. It was easy to believe the Beastie Boys were dead as a group, which may explain a persistent rumor that circulated in 1988 that Mike D had expired of a drug overdose (or been murdered by members of Run DMC). Diamond referenced the rumor on "Shake Your Rump" from *Paul's Boutique*: "I'm Mike D and I'm back from the dead." The group was particularly offended by an article in *Spin*, a hip-hop map of America (which I commissioned and edited but didn't write), which referred to Los Angeles as "home of retired rappers the Beastie Boys."

Mike Diamond kept a close eye on developments in New York's hip-hop scene, scoping out the competition. Since *Licensed to Ill* came out in 1986, the hip-hop landscape had dramatically changed. Every month it seemed like new ground was being broken by somebody. Digital sampling had opened up a whole new world of creative possibilities. With hip-hop's sonic palette expanding all the time, it was no longer good enough just to have a beat and a rhyme. Sometimes less isn't more; sometimes more is more. One album above all others symbolized this new direction: *It Takes A Nation Of Millions To Hold Us Back* by Public Enemy.

Chuck D preached revolution but Public Enemy's producer Hank Shocklee had created one. With *It Takes A Nation Of Millions To Hold Us Back*, he hadn't just rewritten the rulebook on how to make a hip-hop record, he'd torn it up and replaced it with his own.

When Mike Diamond first got the album he couldn't stop listening to it. Damn, he thought, this makes *Licensed to Ill* sound like a compilation album, just a collection of songs. He would play it over and over on his headphones to understand how the record's producer, Hank Shocklee, had done this, even though it made him depressed. How could the Beastie Boys hope to compete with this, he thought to himself. Yet it also excited the music fan in him, made him feel thrilled that such great music can exist in the world. *It Takes A Nation Of Millions To Hold Us Back* was the first time he'd ever heard a rap group approach the album format like a rock group.

The Beastie Boys now had a twofold objective: not just to escape Rick Rubin's shadow but also to make an album that could compete at the highest level with hip-hop heavyweights like Public Enemy.

❝ We've gotta to make another record, otherwise how we gonna get into all these U2 parties? ❞ MCA

The discovery process of the case was beginning and Def Jam lawyers wanted to grill the three about why they had broken a legally binding contract that obliged them to deliver seven more albums to Def Jam.

Capitol Records executives had also began to wonder why there was a delay. They hadn't heard any new songs in months. Half the tracks had already been cut by the Dust Brothers before the Beastie Boys had even arrived in L.A. All the trio had to do was come up with some rhymes to rap over the top but, reportedly, they were suffering from writer's block. Label president David Berman was starting to regret ever having considered signing the Beastie Boys. This was turning into a fiasco. He knew his job was on the line.

Only after the Beasties moved from Le Mondrian to a house in the Hollywood Hills near Mulholland Drive did the group really knuckle down and get to work on the album. They christened the new place the G.Spot because of the monogrammed giant "G" on the gate. The Beastie Boys rented the house from a kind but eccentric elderly couple, Alex and Caroline Grashof. The spread was a monument to 1970s bad taste. The most unusual feature was the sunken bedroom in the guesthouse, with a large picture window that looked out onto the swimming pool below the water line. The underwater photograph on the inside cover

of *Paul's Boutique* was shot from inside the sunken bedroom.

Even better, the Grashofs had left behind a veritable treasure-trove of outrageously tacky outfits they had bought in the 1970s. The outfits were said to have inspired the similar outfits the trio wore in the video for "Hey Ladies." Caroline Grasof was not pleased when she found out that the Beastie Boys had been rifling through her wardrobes. "Have your girlfriends been wearing my clothes?" she demanded to know.

One night, a drunken Mike D accidentally ran his car into the house's metal gate. Mario Caldato Jr, the engineer on *Paul's Boutique*, suggested that a high school buddy of his, Mark Ramos Nishita, could fix the gate. While he was working, Nishita happened to mention he fixed vintage synthesizers and he knew how to play them. That's how Keyboard Money Mark became the unofficial fourth member of the Beastie Boys.

Yauch was probably joking when he told *LA Weekly* in 1989 that what prompted the Beastie Boys to stop goofing around and get down to business was the time they were denied entry to a U2 party because the bouncers didn't recognize them: "It's like, we were the big shit, right, and then like Bon Jovi and U2 and those motherfuckers got big and we rolled up to this U2 party and they wouldn't even let us in and we said: 'Fuck

MCA

“ Adam served as a great example for myself and for so much of what determination, faith, focus, and humility coupled with a sense of humor can accomplish. The world is in need of many more like him. ” MIKE D

“ Yauch was in charge. He was smarter, more organized. In a group of friends, you all come up with stupid shit to do. But you never do it. With Yauch, it got done. He had that extra drive to see things through. We each had our roles. One of his was the make-it-happen person. ” AD-ROCK

OPPOSITE: Budding rapper: MCA live onstage in L.A., California, 1986.

ABOVE, RIGHT: Fighting for his right to party, 1990.

RIGHT: MCA performing at the Pukkelpop festival, Hasselt, Belgium, 1992.

BOUTIQUE COMPLETE

Between the bong hits, the cigarettes, and the LSD; the coffee and the red wine; and the whippets and the magic mushrooms, the atmosphere must have been like a scene from a Hunter S. Thompson book—*Fear and Loathing in Hollywood*—in Matt Dike's second-floor railroad apartment in the last three months of 1988. This time, however, it was a controlled craziness. Everybody had their heads in the groove, looking for the finishing line. They knew where they were going at last. They just needed to get there before they were engulfed by madness.

At the end of a narrow dark hallway, Matt Dike was in his bedroom sourcing samples while surrounded by stacks of vinyl. He was looking for the perfect piece of bass or the perfect scrap of drums or the perfect snippet of guitar. His vast record collection—vinyl platters stacked in crates as high as the ceiling —was the primary source for all the samples on *Paul's Boutique*. The incredible range of music that was sampled for the album—the Beatles, Sly and the Family Stone, the Ramones, Pink Floyd, the Eagles, Curtis Mayfield, Jimi Hendrix, Kurtis Blow, Led Zeppelin, Donovan, Johnny Cash, to name a few— was a tribute to Dike's eclectic taste.

Simpson and King were in the living room, looping and layering samples, taking bits of old sounds and meticulously synchronizing them together to make a new sound, building the edifice that would become *Paul's Boutique*, sonic brick by sonic brick. The duo would take hours and hours just to line up one loop with another. Three drum tracks played simultaneously, a bass line lay buried under another bass line, samples were disguised so cleverly that it would take the digital fingerprinting technology of the future to uncover them. What should have been a recipe for unlistenable cacophony was, in their hands, to borrow a line from Nina Simone, funkier than a mosquito's tweeter.

The Beastie Boys were over in the corner furiously writing and rhyming, getting ready to step into the closet that doubled as a vocal booth. The imagery they were creating this time around was much more evocative and precise than in the past: "Wonder Bread shoes and singing Helter Skelter," to describe a homeless person and "Sweating like sardines in a flophouse fraternity,'" to describe what it's like to be stuck between stations on the New York subway during the summer. The interplay between the three of them was almost telepathic by this point as they finished each other's sentences, swapping phrases back and forth, bouncing words and images off each other like it was raining ping-pong balls. Maybe all that time

playing table tennis in the studio when they were supposed to be working was practice for the album.

By the beginning of 1989, *Paul's Boutique* was practically finished. The very last stop was the Record Plant in Hollywood for the final mix. Mike D saw one final chance to stick it to Capitol Records. He rented the biggest and most expensive studio he could find for $15,000 a day, a studio big enough to record an orchestra, then turned it into a recreational room, complete with an air hockey table, pinball machines, and a ping-pong table. You can hear them playing ping-pong in the background if you listen carefully to the intro of "3-Minute Rule" on *Paul's Boutique*.

Just because the album was complete didn't necessarily mean that the public would ever get to hear it, not if Russell Simmons had his way. He was still furious that Capitol Records had poached his best-selling act and was now threatening to file another lawsuit, this one for copyright infringement, on top of the original lawsuit for breach of contract, which was still winding its way through the court system. As far as Simmons was concerned, *Paul's Boutique* was Def Jam's property and Capitol Records had no right to distribute it.

Moreover, Simmons had hatched a plan that if Capitol did release the album, Def Jam would release its own Beastie Boys album made up of Beastie Boys outtakes, including the two tracks that Columbia had insisted be removed from *Licensed to Ill*, the violent gangster rap song "Scenario" and the Beatles cover, "I'm Down." The album already had a title, *White House,* and Public Enemy's Chuck D and Hank Shocklee were slated as the producers. The Beastie Boys didn't believe Simmons would really follow through, they thought that he was bluffing, just trying to mess with their heads, but if he was angry enough, who knows?

If Simmons did go ahead and release *White House,* the title alone would be enough to stir up controversy. When the Beastie Boys were on Def Jam, the group was largely protected from awkward questions about white privilege and cultural appropriation. If you were on

Def Jam, you were automatically down. Now the group was on Capitol Records, the Beastie Boys were easy targets, especially now that black militancy was on the rise among rappers.

The *White House* project was more real than the Beastie Boys imagined. Chuck D had listened to the outtakes and mapped out

a plan for how to produce them, but backed out of the project after he heard *Paul's Boutique* and was impressed by the Beastie Boys' effort.

"Now that I know they're serious," Chuck D told me at the time, "I'm not going to go ahead with *White House*."

OPPOSITE: Amid rows with record labels, old and new, as well as with each other, the band keep it together... just, 1990.

BELOW: 1989 saw the band get better at ping-pong but become easy targets for the press, and fellow rappers, who doubted their authenticity.

PAUL'S BOUTIQUE : RECEPTION AND LEGACY

The Beastie Boys may have left New York but the spirit of downtown New York hadn't left them, judging by the cover of *Paul's Boutique*. The album was released by Capitol Records on July 25, 1989, in a gorgeous gatefold sleeve that, when folded out, revealed a panoramic view of New York's Lower East Side—at the time this was a poor immigrant neighborhood of tenements and bodegas in the process of being rapidly gentrified by hipsters. The eponymous store depicted on the cover was really Lee's Sportswear at 99 Rivington Street, the same space that two decades later housed a hipster cafe called "Paul's Boutique."

The Beastie Boys name-checked former New York mayor Ed Koch, Shea Stadium, the Yankees, Coney Island, the D Train, and the 1970s basketball player Hawthorne Wingo. They also took a whack at their old Def Jam boss, Russell Simmons: "Smoked up a bag of elephant tranquilizers/Because I had to deal with a money-hungry miser/Had a 'caine-filled Kool with my man Russ Rush/Saw all my teeth fall in the sink when I started to brush."

On "Stop That Train" they rapped about Bernie Goetz, the infamous subway vigilante who shot four black youths in 1984 in a New York subway station ("Caught a bullet in the lung from Bernie Goetz"), and smoking drugs at the St. Anthony Feast street festival on Mulberry Street in SoHo on "Car Thief" ("Smoking a wooly at St. Anthony Feast").

Either the Beastie Boys were homesick or they didn't want their fans to know that they had permanently moved to the Land of the Lotus Eaters.

The follow-up to *Licensed to Ill* also saw the trio mining a deeper and more sonically sophisticated groove. Gone were the barebones beats and crashing guitar chords, replaced by a multilayered collage of sampled sounds that came courtesy of the Dust Brothers. It was so dense, it sounded psychedelic, which may have had something to do with the fact that Adam Yauch had discovered LSD eyedrops and was sharing them with other people in the studio during the recording of the album. The juvenile frat-boy image they'd created for *Licensed to Ill* still occasionally peeked through in some of the lyrics: "Rapunzel Rapunzel let down your hair/So I can climb up and get into your underwear" ("What Comes Around"). Musically, however, the album was so jam-packed with detail, it couldn't have been more different from their minimalist debut. The album proved that the Beastie Boys didn't need Rick Rubin to make a great record, a fact that Rubin himself acknowledged when he first heard *Paul's Boutique*.

The album opens with an understated jazzy groove. The familiar bell-like sound of a Fender Rhodes electric piano (a sample of "Loran's Dance" by Idris Muhammad) emerges slowly from the murky mix. Then a familiar deep voice in an unfamiliar context. It's MCA channeling the spirit of Barry White looking for chocolate love.

"To all the Brooklyn girls"

"To all the French girls"

"To all the Oriental girls"

"To all the Jamaican girls"

He works his way down the list, going country by country, until he gets to: "To all the stewardesses flying around the world."

Bang. A loud drum roll ricochets off the walls (a sample of Alphonse Mouzon's "Funky Snakefoot"). Boom. A thumping bass hits you in the pit of your stomach. Zoom. You're off on a funky magic carpet ride called "Shake Your Rump" accompanied by a fat fuzzy bass courtesy of Rose Royce and some psychedelic imagery courtesy of Mike D. "I'm in a lava lamp, inside my brain hotel. I might be freakin' or peakin', but I rock well."

After many wild detours and abrupt course corrections, 40 minutes later the listener arrives breathless at the final destination, "B-Boy Bouillabaisse," the most

ambitious track on the album, a melody of nine songs, which runs the gamut, from a trip down memory lane to visit the Beastie Boys' old rehearsal space in New York's Chinatown, "59 Chrystie Street;" to a gritty evocation of a ride on the D Train to Coney Island, "Stop That Train;" to the first spiritual stirrings of Adam Yauch on "A Year And A Day".

Because it was buried at the back of the album, fans and critics didn't pay much attention to "A Year And A Day" when it came out, but in hindsight, the song provides an intriguing glimpse into the mind of a man at the beginning of a spiritual journey that would drastically change the Beastie Boys in ways nobody could have imagined. Yauch's vocals are heavily distorted on "A Year And A Day" (he recorded the song wearing a jet pilot's helmet outfitted with a microphone) but the lyrics—"I am going to the limits of my ultimate destiny/Feeling as though somebody were testing me"—have a poignancy that's almost tragic, given what we know now.

As expected, the critical reaction to *Paul's Boutique* was overwhelmingly positive. John Leland writing for *Spin* magazine raved, "In a thinking man's world, this is a position paper for the late-Eighties avant-garde: a bricolage of samples and styles (from Public Enemy to Led Zeppelin), a mix that talks back to the rappers, a constantly changing relationship between the artist and the artifact. In a knucklehead world, it's a crashing party album with more dumb stuff than you ever imagined. In the in-between world, where you and I live, it throws smart and stupid in the mix with everything else —hard rock, hip-hop, spoken word, dust visions and cheeba dreams, loose girlies and giant hi-tech fart noises—and dares you to keep up...Long overrated as a gimmick, the Beastie Boys have been underrated as visionary grubs. This is the sound of three guys working very hard, cramming each second with new ideas and a tough rhyme."

Rolling Stone's David Handelman compared the album to the Beatles' *Abbey Road*: "Yet with the dense, crafty *Paul's Boutique*, the Beasties reinvent the turntable and prove they're here to stay."In *Playboy*, journalist Robert Christgau wasn't quite as effusive, saying that *Paul's Boutique* "doesn't jump you the way great rap usually does," but congratulated them for "bearing down on the cleverest rhymes in the biz." Christgau later gave *Paul's Boutique* an "A" grade in his *Robert Christgau's Consumer Guide* and wrote, "Jam-packed, frenetic, stark, the sequel isn't as user-friendly. But give it three plays and half a j's worth of concentration, and its high-speed volubility and riffs from nowhere will amaze and delight you. It's an absolutely unpretentious affirmation of cultural diversity, of where they came from and where they went from there."

The Beastie Boys had reinvented hip-hop as the sonic science of the future wrapped in the retro-funk of the past, but was anybody listening other than critics?

"Hey Ladies" was the first single from *Paul's Boutique*. The single was an ingenious mash-up that sampled everyone from the Bar-Kays to Deep Purple, Kool and the Gang to a snippet from Sweet's "Ballroom Blitz" ("She thinks she's the passionate one"). Halfway through, the song breaks down into the funkiest cowbell solo this side of go-go masters Trouble Funk. It was released in June as part of an EP, *Love, American Style*, but only rose to 36 on the *Billboard Hot 100*. The song was accompanied by a hilarious video, a campy ode to 1970s sartorial excess, featuring Yauch, Diamond, and Horovitz wearing disco outfits and candy-colored pimp costumes. The group had gotten heavily into 1970s movies and one of their favorite actors was Rudy Ray Moore, the X-rated comedian who played the loquacious pimp Dolemite in the 1975 blaxploitation movie of the same name.

The problem was that very few Americans in 1989 were nostalgic for the 1970s, a decade that was remembered mainly as a series

> ## "The band's agenda all along was to make an album that signaled a clean break with the Def Jam era and that would forever take them out of Rick Rubin's shadow to establish them as artists in their own right."

of never-ending crises: the Iran hostage crisis, the energy crisis, the stagflation crisis, etc. Fans of "(You Got To) Fight For Your Right (To Party!)" must have scratched their heads in bemusement when they saw the video on MTV and then turned to another channel, which was probably the effect the Beastie Boys were intending. The 1970s revival wouldn't get into full swing until the next decade, when it became the default setting for a certain type of ironic hipster culture. As usual, the Beastie Boys were ahead of the times.

Even worse, *Paul's Boutique* looked like it wasn't even going to go gold, let alone achieve the quadruple-platinum status of *Licensed to Ill*. Capitol Records had shipped a million copies but within a month many of these copies were being returned by record stores. *Paul's Boutique* reached number 15 on the *Billboard Pop Charts* and then plummeted like a rock. After three months, Capitol Records stopped promoting the album: *Paul's Boutique* was done.

The mistake that Capitol made was thinking that the Beastie Boys wanted to replicate the success of their debut album. But they were never interested in making *Licensed to Ill 2* and relive that Beastie-mania madness. Hell, no. Their agenda all along was to make an album that signaled a clean break with the Def Jam era and that would forever take them out from under Rick Rubin's shadow to establish them as artists in their own right. Viewed that way, *Paul's Boutique* was a fabulous success.

It would take a few more years for the public to finally realize what a groundbreaking collection *Paul's Boutique* was, and remains. Today, it's widely regarded as one of the best—if not the best— albums of the Beastie Boys' career and would eventually go on to sell two million copies. In 2005, *Spin* ranked it number 12 on the magazine's "100 Greatest Albums" and it made the list of *Time* magazine's "100 Greatest Albums of All Time". In 2009, a special 20th anniversary edition of *Paul's Boutique* was released. *Rolling Stone* re-reviewed the album and upped the original four-star rating to five stars, calling it "a hip-hop masterpiece."Jazz giant Miles Davis told *Vibe* magazine that *Paul's Boutique* was an album he never tired of listening to. Producer Eric B, of Eric B and Rakim, told Russell Simmons that he could have made 15 albums with the ideas from *Paul's Boutique*.

One of the reasons the album still sounds so fresh is that it would be impossible to reproduce what the Dust Brothers did today without spending millions of dollars in copyright fees. What is now called the Golden Age of hip-hop, roughly the period between 1987 and 1992, was based in large part on

the artistic freedom to sample multiple sources without fear of litigation. That changed in 1991 with the landmark case of Grand Upright Music, Ltd. v. Warner Bros. Records Inc. Before this case, hip-hop artists who routinely took snippets of other musicians' work and rearranged them to create something new, relied on the "fair use doctrine" to protect themselves from lawsuits filed by copyright holders whose work they had sampled. The fair use doctrine protects limited use of other people's copyrighted material. Albums like De La Soul's *Three Feet High and Rising* and Public Enemy's *It Takes A Nation of Millions...*, as well as *Paul's Boutique*, all depended on a liberal interpretation of the fair use doctrine without which they could not have existed.

Grand Upright Music, Ltd. v. Warner Bros. Records Inc. pitted Irish singer-songwriter Gilbert O'Sullivan against Brooklyn rapper Biz Markie, who had sampled O'Sullivan's 1972 hit "Alone Again (Naturally)" for his song "Alone Again." Biz Markie's record label Cold Chillin' had approached O'Sullivan and asked for permission to use the song. O'Sullivan said go ahead and make the track and if he liked it, he would give his permission. When he heard the finished product, he hated it. He thought the comic rapper was making fun of his song, but Cold Chillin' went ahead and released "Alone Again" over O'Sullivan's objections.

The judge ruled for O'Sullivan and even referred the case to the U.S. Attorney's office for criminal prosecution because the judge thought the infringement was so egregious. The ruling meant that any samples in the future had to be pre-approved by the copyright holder. Those who didn't not only faced civil penalties but also the possibility of criminal prosecution.

The sonic landscape of hip-hop, which was built on samples, changed practically overnight. Using dozens of samples from different sources, as the Dust Brothers routinely did, became a thing of the past. Now, it was only economically feasible to use one or two samples on a song, especially since copyright holders started demanding outrageously high fees, in a handful of cases as much as 100 percent of the royalties. The Golden Age of hip-hop was dead, thanks to Grand Upright Music, Ltd. v. Warner Bros. Records Inc.

THE FALLOUT FROM *PAUL'S BOUTIQUE*

In Autumn 1989 CEO Joe Smith fired Capitol president David Berman who had signed off on the controversial $3 million Beastie Boys deal. He also canned the entire A&R department. The Beastie Boys went to see Berman's replacement, Hale Milgrim, to ask for help in promoting *Paul's Boutique.* "Sorry," he told the band. Donny Osmond had a comeback album coming out soon and the company needed to get behind that release. Capitol refused to put any more money into the album. That's why the Beastie Boys never got to tour in support of *Paul's Boutique,* except for a handful of disastrous and humiliating nightclub performances.

As 1989 ended, the Def Jam lawsuit was finally settled. Def Jam agreed to release the Beastie Boys from their contract. In return, Def Jam got to keep all the royalties from *Licensed to Ill.* The Beastie Boys had bought their freedom but at a huge cost.

After the commercial failure of *Paul's Boutique*, the Beastie Boys used what was left of the Capitol Records advance to build a studio in an old ballroom in Atwater Village, a neighborhood in northeast Los Angeles, next to the Los Angeles River. The Beastie Boys didn't want to spend money on expensive L.A. recording studios. The new studio was christened G-Son after a plumbing store next to the ballroom called Gilsons, whose store sign was missing the letters "I" and "L."

The Beastie Boys spend much of 1990 and 1991 jamming together, returning to their pre-digital punk rock roots. Mike D played drums, Yauch was on bass, Horovitz on guitar. Keyboard Money Mark joined in the sessions as the fourth member of the band, playing rare analog synthesizers, an old sound that sounded new again to the Beastie Boys' ears. Yauch had rekindled his interest in being in a band after he played bass on "3-Minute Rule" from *Paul's Boutique*. Horovitz played guitar on "Looking Down The Barrel Of A Gun". This was the first time since their hardcore days that they had played together as a band. These sessions became the basis for the Beasties' next album *Check Your Head.*

There was another reason the Beastie Boys were going analog. Their lawyers had warned them that if their next album contained so many samples they wouldn't earn any money. So for *Check Your Head*, they were planning on using only a small number of samples.

Capitol Records didn't expect *Check Your Head* to be a hit, but the label would be pleasantly surprised. The Beastie Boys were about to become big again, not among beer-guzzling meatheads but with a different crowd—alternative music fans, a growing segment of the music-buying public.

The 1990s saw the Zeitgeist finally catch up with the Beastie Boys—the insider irony, the obscure pop culture references, the self-conscious kitsch, and the twisted comedy of *Paul's Boutique* turned into the lingua franca of 1990s cool. A number of musical trends the band pioneered—using real instruments on hip-hop records, combining rap, rock, and funk, the rediscovery of analog musical instruments—became all the rage.

Yauch, Diamond, and Horovitz also turned into unlikely style icons among the anti-fashion set. They were rocking trucker caps, tight jeans, and three-day-old stubble years before it became the official uniform of urban hipsters everywhere. The Beastie Boys practically invented scruffy cool. Old school sneakers, baggy chinos, polyester shirts, vintage NBA and NFL sports uniforms, you name it, the Beastie Boys wore them first. They were being affectionately ironic about 1970s pop culture when Quentin Tarantino was still a video clerk. By 1994, *New York* magazine was saying: "The Beastie Boys have come to define an entire generational aesthetic."

Most surprising of all, in the 1990s the Beastie Boys also became improbable leaders of a new social justice movement among the twenty-something generation.

“ I realize we were supposed to come out with "Fight for Your Right to Party, Part Two" and fall on our faces. Sorry to disappoint everyone. „ MIKE D

1992
CHECK YOUR HEAD

After *Paul's Boutique*, it was three years before the trio released their next album. *Check Your Head* was a return to the band's punk rock roots, and is regularly voted as one of the best records of the nineties.

1.	Jimmy James	3:14
2.	Funky Boss	1:35
3.	Pass The Mic	4:17
4.	Gratitude	2:45
5.	Lighten Up	2:41
6.	Finger Lickin' Good	3:39
7.	So What'cha Want	3:37
8.	The Biz vs. The Nuge	0:33
9.	Time for Livin'	1:48
10.	Something's Got To Give	3:28
11.	The Blue Nun	0:32
12.	Stand Together	2:47
13.	POW!	2:13
14.	The Maestro	2:52
15.	Groove Holmes	2:33
16.	Live At P.J.'s	3:18
17.	Mark On The Bus	1:05
18.	Professor Booty	4:13
19.	In 3's	2:23
20.	Namasté	4:01

OPPOSITE: Despite some mixed reviews, Check Your Head gained the band a brand new audience: Generation X.

THE MAKING OF *CHECK YOUR HEAD*

The Beastie Boys' third album *Check Your Head*—which takes its name from the time Adam Yauch brought a pack of Desert Storm trading cards to the studio and Mark Ramos Nishita, aka Keyboard Money Mark, put a tick next to the head of General Norman Schwarzkopf—signaled yet another new direction for these musical magpies. The group had replaced the orchestral montaging of *Paul's Boutique* with a more opaque and deliberately ramshackle vibe, augmenting the usual sampled sounds with live instruments they played themselves: Mike D on drums, Yauch on bass, Horovitz on guitar, and Keyboard Money Mark on Hammond organ and Moog synthesizer. This new direction was immediately apparent from the album cover, which featured a black-and-white photograph of the Beastie Boys sitting on a curb with guitar cases by their side. The 20-song collection was culled from a series of lengthy jam sessions that took place over a three-year period producing a hundred hours of audio tape. The band would then sample the parts of the jams they liked and loop them to make the foundation for the songs.

BELOW: The band rock the Roseland in New York City, 1992.

OPPOSITE: 1998, and the band perform their climactic encore at the Pukkelpop festival, Hasselt, Belgium.

"We wanted to make it like a break-beats record," Mike D explained when I interviewed the band for New York Newsday in 1992. "The same way as when you sample you take the best bit of a song, we wanted each song to contain the best bits from our jam sessions."

A common argument at the time was that sampling de-skills musicians. Why bother learning to play an instrument, claimed opponents of digital sampling, when you could simply steal somebody else's musicianship. Mike D said that exactly the opposite was true of the Beastie Boys. Sampling had in reality spurred the band to take up live instruments again for the first time since their pre-Def Jam days. "When you sample the type of music we do, you come to respect the incredible musicianship that went into the original," he said. "And you want to be able to play like that."

That's not to say sampling other people's material was absent from the album—"Funky Boss" sampled the comedian Richard Pryor, "Finger Lickin' Good" sampled Bob Dylan's "Just Like Tom Thumb's Blues," the intro of "Pass The Mic" sampled Bad Brains' "Big Take Over". The opening track, "Jimmy James" (so-named after Jimi Hendrix's first band Jimmy James and the Blue Flames), was at first almost entirely made up of Jimi Hendrix samples, but after the Hendrix estate refused to allow the guitarist's music to be used on the album, the band had to re-record the track by trying to recreate some of the samples live in the studio. (The original version was later released as a 12-inch single after the Hendrix estate relented.)

This time out, the Beastie Boys placed less emphasis on rapping and a lot more emphasis on the music. The words were

When you sample the type of music we do, you come to respect the incredible musicianship that went into the original. ” MIKE D

just another element in the mix, not the main focus, which might account for why the lyrics sounded like an afterthought on a few of the tracks. Gone was the clever wordplay that once characterized their raps. There was still a touch of standard-issue B-Boy braggadocio, but judging by such lines as "I've got more spice than the Frugal Gourmet," their heart wasn't in it anymore. For one song, "Time for Livin," recorded with the obscure hardcore band Frontline, rather than writing original lyrics, Mike D simply lifted the words wholesale from "Small Talk" by Sly and the Family Stone. Also, the rhymes were often heavily distorted. On "So What'cha Want," when Mike D raps "I'm thinking I'm losing my mind, this time/I think I'm losing my mind," he sounds like he is speaking through a malfunctioning

megaphone. Also gone were the tales of teenage hi-jinks that made Licensed to Ill such a hoot. The Beastie Boys had matured. On "Namasté", listening to MCA recite a druggy poem with lines like "A butterfly floats on the breeze of a sunlit sky/As I feel this reality gently fade away" over a backing track reminiscent of The Doors, it was difficult to remember that this was a group that had once scandalized Middle America with its bawdy antics.

Still, if the lyrics weren't the Beastie Boys at their wittiest, the music more than made up for it—a loose-limbed, lo-fi collection that combined funk, punk, progressive rock, heavy metal, jazzy lounge music, and hip-hop, sometimes to startlingly original effect. Some tracks sounded so purposely muddy it was as if they were recorded underwater or at the bottom of a well—a

very different sound from the digitally perfect products that came out of recording studios at the time.

"Nowadays everybody wants this real hype digital equipment," Mike D said, "but we outfitted our studio with all this really cheap equipment, like clavinets, old drum kits, fuzz basses, and wah-wah pedals."

The Beastie Boys had discovered a store on Larchmont Avenue in Los Angeles that sold secondhand guitar pedals from the 1960s and 1970s. The group was particularly fond of the Maestro G-2 Rhythm 'n' Sound, an effects unit that, when a guitar was plugged into it, created a fuzzy sound similar to Keith Richards famous guitar line on the Rolling Stones' "(I Can't Get No) Satisfaction. (Richards actually used an earlier version of the device, the Maestro Fuzz-Tone). The Beastie Boys even named a song on *Check Your Head* after the little box, "The Maestro."

Work on *Check Your Head*, which would take three years to complete, began in the aftermath of the infamous meeting with the newly appointed Capitol Records' president Hale Milgrim who told the group not to expect any additional promotion

underscored the feeling in the band that, for their next album, they needed to establish themselves conclusively as musicians in their own right, separate from any hotshot producer.

At Horovitz's apartment, the Beastie Boys began to rehearse the material that later became *Check Your Head*. The trio was joined by keyboardist Money Mark (Nishita) and they would jam together into the early hours trying to duplicate, using live instruments, the funky sounds they had sampled on Paul's Boutique. Funk is a superficially simple genre that is difficult to play well. It not only takes stamina but also a level of musicianship that was beyond the Beastie Boys at this stage in their development. Many funk musicians, such as The Crusaders and Donald Byrd, initially trained as jazz musicians, and those that didn't, like The Meters and Jimi Hendrix, honed their craft playing gig after gig on the grueling "chitlin circuit," a network of Southern clubs. The Beastie Boys had been listening to bands like The Meters and The Crusaders and, while they knew they couldn't match these groups for musical ability, they thought that with enough practice they could create a good-enough approximation of the classic funk sound of the 1970s.

After Horovitz's neighbors complained about the noise coming from his apartment, the group realized they needed somewhere else to get their groove on, so they rented space at the Atwater Community Center, above a drugstore on a commercial stretch of Glendale Avenue in a lower-middle-class neighborhood called Atwater Village. The place used to be a ballroom, and the band took over the main dance floor, which already had a stage at one end, where they set up their instruments.

The idea was to create a combination recording studio and hangout spot, where the group could leisurely pursue their new direction without having to worry about eating up expensive studio time. By this point, the Beastie Boys weren't exactly living in poverty, but they needed to cut back on expenses, given the commercial failure of *Paul's Boutique* and the $2million dollars in royalties from *Licensed to Ill* that they agreed to let Def Jam keep in return for breaking their contract with the label. As luck would have it, Keyboard Money Mark wasn't just a talented keyboardist. He was also a master carpenter, who built sets for a living. With stacks of plywood and a nail gun in hand, he began constructing the recording studio to the Beastie Boys' exact specifications—first a control room, then a drum shack, then a kitchen, and then, finally, the most unusual feature of the studio, an indoor basketball court and a skateboarding ramp.

The band continued to jam as G-Son studio was being built by Keyboard Money Mark, who after he finished his day job constructing the facility, would put down his nail gun and join them for a nighttime jam. The Beastie Boys paid tribute to Keyboard Money Mark on "Finger Lickin' Good" from *Check Your Head*: "You know he ain't having it, just give him some wood and he'll build you a cabinet." Money Mark also brought into G-Son a number of vintage keyboards and

for *Paul's Boutique* because the label needed to concentrate on pushing the new Donny Osmond record. Milgrim suggested they forget about Paul's Boutique and instead start to make their next album, which is exactly what the group did.

By this point, the band had left the G-Son and were no longer living together. Yauch had moved into a log cabin in the Hollywood Hills, Diamond bought a big house in Los Feliz Hills, and Horovitz was living in a Koreatown apartment. The Beastie boys had no desire to replicate the sample-heavy sound of Paul's Boutique not only because, after Grand Upright Music, Ltd. v. Warner Bros. Records Inc, it would be prohibitively expensive to do so, but also because they'd had a falling out with the Dust Brothers over money and credit for the album. While nowhere near as acrimonious as their split with Rick Rubin, the dispute synthesizers that would become a key element of the sound on *Check Your Head*.

The beef between the Beastie Boys and the Dust Brothers didn't prevent them from hiring Mario Caldato Jr, the engineer on *Paul's Boutique*, as the producer for *Check Your Head*. At first, Caldato was puzzled why the Beastie Boys were intent on using such cheap, old-fashioned equipment, why everything had to sound so scuzzy, but after a while he just went with the flow. After all, his job was to facilitate the Beastie Boys' vision, not to impose his own views, which was exactly the attitude the band was looking for in a producer.

In marked contrast to their experience making *Paul's Boutique*, the Beastie Boys felt little pressure from the record company to deliver an album. There were no A&R people visiting the G-Son studio anxiously enquiring about how the album was progressing. So leisurely was the progress, Caldato and Keyboard Money Mark presumed that Capitol Records hadn't set a date for the delivery of the album. Just as well, since the Beastie Boys did not work well under deadline pressure. By this point Capitol executives had resigned themselves to writing off the losses that the Beastie Boys had incurred with *Paul's Boutique*. The band's contract required them to deliver one more album. After that, it would be "Bye, bye, Beastie Boys," never to darken Capitol's doorstep ever again.

The Beastie Boys initially thought about releasing *Check Your Head* without any vocals. "There was talk of making it an instrumental record for a while," said Mike D on the album commentary that accompanied the *Check Your Head* re-release in 2009. "For the first year and a half where we just came into the studio and played our instruments every day, we didn't even mess with vocals for a long time."

"The climate was kind of weird in hip-hop when we went in to do *Check Your Head*," Adam Yauch had said. "A lot of the hip-hop that was coming out was really angry, and we felt a little alienated from that. That's why there were plans for the album to be instrumental."

As they got further into the recording, the Beastie Boys started to listen to hip-hop albums by A Tribe Called Quest and Public Enemy. They started thinking about laying some raps over the instrumental cuts. A visit from an old friend Biz Markie—the comic rapper whose song, "Alone Again" was at the center of the Grand Upright Music, Ltd. v. Warner Bros. Records Inc case—made up their minds for them. The Biz guest

OPPOSITE: The Beastie Boys pose outside the Roseland, New York, 1992.

ABOVE: The trio review the latest releases, 1992. Rollins Band's "Low Self Opinion" receives record of the week.

RIGHT: The band's international success, thanks in part to "Sabotage," handed them headline festival slots all over Europe and the Far East, Pukkelpop festival, Belgium, 1998.

starred on *Check Your Head*'s "The Biz v The Nuge," which also featured gonzo guitarist Ted Nugent. Nugent was also a friend of the band going back to the Madonna tour when the Beastie Boys met him for the first time backstage in Detroit. Nugent just happened to be in town at the same time as the Biz. "They managed to both be at our studio jamming with each other," Yauch said. "That was pretty wild. But the high point was actually when Ted Nugent decided to cook us all dinner, and he cooked up a big bouillabaisse. Biz tasted it and thought it was terrible. He went out and bought himself a bag of candy."

But, as happened with *Paul's Boutique*, the group was suffering from writer's block, so in May 1991 they left G-Son and moved temporarily to a beach house near San Francisco, to see if a change of scenery might get their creative juices flowing. While there, they heard some shocking news: Davis Scilken, whom Horovitz played with in a band called the Young and the Useless before he joined the Beastie Boys, had died of a drug overdose only days after getting out of rehab. Horovitz was at high school with Scilken where they became best friends. Scilken was by the band's side throughout the madness that was the *Licensed to Ill* tour, appearing in the "(You Got To) Fight For Your Right (To Party!)" video and performing the job of "trim coordinator"—scouting the crowd for pretty girls to bring backstage to meet the Beastie Boys. Scilken was name-checked on "Looking Down The Barrel Of A Gun" on Paul's Boutique: "Coordinating trim is my man Dave Scilken."

The Beastie Boys returned to New York for Scilken's funeral and, while there, re-united with Kate Schellenbach who had been unceremoniously dumped from the group by Rick Rubin before the release of *Licensed to Ill*. Schellenbach had found a new gig, drumming for Luscious Jackson. She didn't blame Diamond, Yauch or Horovitz for her ouster but Rubin, whom she called "a sexist pig." Scilken's death inspired some serious soul-searching among the Beastie Boys about their own sometimes reckless lifestyles. His passing also motivated the band to finally finish the album, which they dedicated to Scilken.

By the summer of 1991, the album was finally coming to fruition. However, after nearly two years of jamming almost daily, the group was tired so they decided to take a break. Adam Yauch, an avid outdoorsman, went on holiday to Nepal to snowboard in the Himalayas. While in the mountains, he happened to meet a group of Tibetans who were fleeing across the border from China to a refugee camp in Katmandu. The stories the Tibetans told about the Chinese oppression of Tibetan Buddhists deeply touched him. He became determined to use the platform the Beastie Boys provided to highlight the decades-long struggle of the Tibetan people to free themselves from Chinese rule.

"I didn't know anything about Tibet at all," Yauch briefed the Chicago Tribune years later. "But I was struck by how these people carried themselves. I began to learn about their nonviolent approach to life, and the teachings of the Dalai Lama."

Yauch returned to California a changed man. Initially, Diamond and Horovitz were politely skeptical. They had an album to finish and didn't need to get sidetracked by Yauch's spiritual odyssey, which had been ongoing since *Paul's Boutique* was completed. Yauch had at first studied the Bible and then delved into Native American religious practices. He became increasingly introspective after he started hanging out at esoteric bookstores in Los Angeles. He was searching for something but what exactly? He now appeared to have found it.

The Beastie Boys rushed to finish the album. Among the last tracks recorded were "Pass The Mic" and "So What'cha Want," the two catchiest tracks on the record. The Beastie Boys had learned the lesson of *Paul's Boutique*. They knew they needed a couple of commercial singles to sell the album.

Finally, after three years in the making, *Check Your Head* hit the record stores. Critical opinion was deeply divided. *Rolling Stone* was enthusiastic, opining, "The cross-pollination of styles on *Check Your Head* is confusing at times, yet the album achieves distinction because of its ingenuity. Beneath the seeming chaos, the Beastie Boys have created a harmonious playground out of their musical fantasies." The hip-hop

magazine *The Source* also put in a good word for *Check Your Head*: "The Beastie Boys pick up instruments and create the guitar and keyboard funk sessions that are the album's true vibe." *The Village Voice* called it "a masterpiece."

Other publications were less complimentary. *Time* magazine thought the album was disappointing: "Six years after their debut, rap's original brats look back to the future, with blurred results" while the *Los Angeles Times* said *Check Your Head* "sounds as if it were recorded in a single afternoon, with time out for a beer." More important than what the critics thought, was the fans' take on the album, if the Beastie Boys had any fans left after the poor showing of *Paul's Boutique*. As it turned out, they did. The lo-tech punk-funk feel of *Check Your Head*, the very quality that the mainstream critics disliked about the album, introduced the Beastie Boys to a new audience: the Lollapalooza generation for whom unpolished music automatically signaled authenticity. Nineteen ninety-two was the year that indie rock was rechristened "alternative rock" and broke out of its college radio ghetto. A niche market turned into a mainstream phenomenon. Nirvana's "Smells Like Teen Spirit" was hailed as a generational anthem. Whether by

chance or design, the Beastie Boys' new more gritttier-sounding direction perfectly positioned the group to surf the wave of what was now the fastest-growing genre on the music scene.

By the following year, the album had sold more than a million copies, no doubt helped by the band who toured relentlessly in support of the album, the first time they had hit the road since *Licensed to Ill*, as well as the constant rotation of "Pass The Mic" on MTV, which later led to an MTV award nomination.

The trio were back on top and this time on their own terms. Without Rick Rubin or the Dust Brothers behind the mixing desk, *Check Your Head* showed that the Beastie Boys had finally become captains of their own musical destiny. Yauch, Diamond, and Horovitz had at last found a vibe that was uniquely their own, a groove they would come to perfect on their next two albums, *Ill Communication* and *Hello Nasty*.

OPPOSITE ABOVE: With Keyboard Money Mark, about to tape a recording for MTV, to promote *Check Your Head*, 1992.

BELOW: Guilty of rocking the Generation X fashions, 1992.

ABOVE: Backstage, with DJ Hurricane, before their infamous performance at the Reading Festival, August 1992.

GRAND ROYAL

The success of *Check Your Head* allowed the Beastie Boys to start their own boutique record label, Grand Royal. No matter how famous or successful they became, Yauch, Horovitz, and Diamond always remained passionate music fans at heart. "The whole thing with being a fan of music and buying records is that you're constantly coming across grooves or records that are gonna change your life," Mike D once said. When they found an album or an artist that excited them, they naturally wanted to share it with other music fans. Grand Royal was their way of turning on their followers to the sounds they were listening to themselves. The first release was *In Search Of Manny* by Luscious Jackson, featuring former Beastie Boys drummer Kate Schellenbach.

Mike D told *Select* magazine how the label originated: "We used to sit for hours coming up with these ideas. But, we never did anything about it. Then Jill Cunniff [Luscious Jackson's lead singer] kept asking if we knew anyone who might put the [Luscious Jackson] demo out and suddenly we thought, 'Why don't we do it?' The fact that we actually did something was miraculous."

Subsequent releases included albums by the hardcore band DFL (Dead Fucking Last), German digital punk group Atari Teenage Riot, legendary New York new wave dance band Liquid Liquid, Japanese rock group Buffalo Daughter, and Russell Simins (not the Def Jam honcho but the drummer from the Jon Spencer Blues Explosion with a similar-sounding name). Even well-known artists like Sean Lennon and Ben Lee recorded for the label.

In 1993, the Beastie Boys debuted a new magazine, also called *Grand Royal*. The initial idea was to create a newsletter for their many fans who flooded the G-Son HQ with letters that never got answered. Along the way it turned into a mishmash of random stuff the Beastie Boys found amusing or hip, a kind of catalog of cool that didn't take itself too seriously: Polaroid cameras, kung-fu, mullet haircuts, Moog synthesizers, the TV show *Kojak*, the free jazz movement, Miami bass music, demolition derbies. The magazine closely mirrored the Beastie Boys' music—packed with in-jokes and obscure pop culture references, willfully eclectic content with a strong retro 1970s vibe running through each issue. The fact that *Grand Royal* was often amateurishly executed only added to its charm, again, just like the Beastie Boys' music.

Interview subjects included such diverse characters as Motor City Madman Ted Nugent, the Tibetan spiritual leader the Dalai Lama, and former basketball superstar Kareem Abdul-Jabbar. If you didn't think a photograph of Burt Reynolds without pants catching a football or a Wu-Tang Clan puzzle page was inherently hilarious, then you weren't part of the publication's intended demographic.

Even the erratic publishing schedule seemed to mimic the Beastie Boys and their notorious aversion to meeting deadlines. After making a big splash with the debut issue, the second issue was over a year late which made it impossible to sell subscriptions and difficult to attract advertisers.

Grand Royal quickly developed a reputation as a kind of training manual for would-be hipsters, or as one wag described it, "The *Martha Stewart Living* for the Hang Ten set", though that makes the magazine sound more cynical and market-driven than it really was. There was a generosity of spirit in the pages of *Grand Royal*; the magazine was in-the-know but never obnoxious.

Mike D compared the magazine to a fine wine, "Each issue is designed to age gracefully, with mellow undertones, and a fruity finish." Adam Yauch disagreed and posted a disclaimer in the magazine, distancing himself from the project. He was upset about a photograph of one of the members of the hip-hop group The Pharcyde brandishing a gun that appeared in the first issue. Not surprisingly, *Grand Royal* produced only six issues in its short five-year lifespan but its legend lives on. Today, copies of the magazine fetch high prices on eBay.

The Beastie Boys also expanded into sidewalk fashion when Mike D invested in X-Large, a line of streetwear that was popular with skateboarders and rappers. The X-Large gorilla logo became an emblem of underground hip, especially after Mike D turned himself into a walking billboard for the company's clothes. From the original store on Vermont Street in Los Angeles, the company opened stores in New York, Seattle, Vancouver, Tokyo, and Cologne, gaining additional cachet when friend of the Beastie Boys, Sonic Youth's Kim Gordon, designed a female clothing line called X-Girl.

The Beastie Boys were no longer just a band but a self-created lifestyle, an attitude, and even a worldview that encompassed not just music but fashion, sports, art, and video. With the magazine, the record label, and the studio housed in the same nondescript building, G-Son became a bustling creative hub that young artists of all genres gravitated toward, to work on the various Beastie Boys side projects. "Our little self-sufficient fantasy world," Mike D liked to call it. The Beastie Boys had created the goofball slacker version of Andy Warhol's Factory, a place where they could do their own thing at whatever speed they chose to do it and without interference from the outside world.

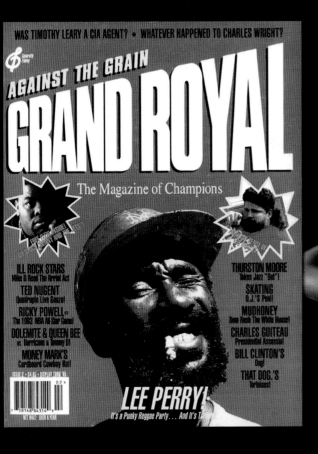

ABOVE: "The magazine of champions": A strong 1970s retro vibe ran through each issue of the band's new magazine, *Grand Royal*, 1993.

OPPOSITE: Green, yellow, and grungy, the band's hairstyles had evolved to suit their new punk rock direction, 1992.

RIGHT: Expanding their portfolio, the trio became rock stars. publishers, label-owners, and fashionistas in 1993.

1994

ILL COMMUNICATION

Regarded as the essential Beastie Boys record, *Ill Communication* turned the band into worldwide superstars. Their second Number One album, and featuring the hit "Sabotage," it was yet another major turning point in the band's career.

1.	Sure Shot	3:19
2.	Tough Guy	0:57
3.	B-Boys Makin' With The Freak Freak	3:36
4.	Bobo On The Corner	1:13
5.	Root Down	3:32
6.	Sabotage	2:58
7.	Get It Together	4:05
8.	Sabrosa	3:29
9.	The Update	3:15
10.	Futterman's Rule	3:42
11.	Alright Hear This	3:06
12.	Eugene's Lament	2:12
13.	Flute Loop	1:54
14.	Do It	3:16
15.	Ricky's Theme	3:43
16.	Heart Attack Man	2:14
17.	The Scoop	3:36
18.	Shambala	3:40
19.	Bodhisattva Vow	3:08
20.	Transitions	2:31

OPPOSITE: Performing "Sabotage" on *Saturday Night Live,* in wigs and mustaches, New York, 1998.

ILL COMMUNICATION

The Beastie Boys often joked among themselves that *Check Your Head* hadn't really taken three years to complete because two of those years were spent playing basketball at their indoor court at G-Son. For their next album, *Ill Communication*, they were in and out of the studio in just over six months which for them was lightning fast. After coming off a grueling eight-month tour, in which they played over a hundred dates to support *Check Your Head*, they were determined to build on the success of that release by pushing out a new album as quickly as they could manage.

First, they needed to rest a while, but by May 1993 they were back in the studio. The more jam-based grooves were recorded at New York's Tin Pan Alley studio. The Beastie Boys then moved to G-Son to cut the hip-hop flavored tracks. By November, the album was complete. In May 1994, it was released just over a year to the day after they started recording—some sort of record for a group not exactly known for its speedy delivery of new material.

In the first week of release, *Ill Communication* entered the *Billboard* album charts at Number One. The Beastie Boys were now officially "the biggest cult band in the world," to borrow a phrase from rock critic Simon Reynolds. It's what they'd wanted ever since they left Def Jam: commercial success without the commercialism. The Beastie Boys had scored their second Number One album but the circumstances of their success couldn't have been more different from the time *Licensed to Ill* hit the top of the charts. There was nobody to take credit for their achievement except themselves. *Ill Communication* was not an album they would have to spend the rest of their careers running away from or feeling ashamed of in any way. It was like they rapped on "Pass The Mic" on *Check Your Head*: "Be true to yourself and you will never fall."

The Beastie Boys had a reputation for constantly redefining their identity. Each of their three previous albums surprised listeners with a sweeping new musical direction, but as Adam Yauch said about *Ill Communication*, "The big surprise is that there is no surprise." Instead, the band built on the sound they debuted on *Check Your Head*—garage-punk-meets-basement-funk, as if the Stooges were jamming with The Meters in the Cavern of Endless Echoes. The Beastie Boys obviously decided they liked the scenery on *Check Your Head* so they decided to stick around for a while to smell the roses but do a little landscaping while they were at it. They weren't intending to break any new ground, but that didn't mean that they couldn't clean out the underbrush, do some pruning, and lay down some new turf.

There are still layers of distortion but they're applied more artfully this time. The music still sounds thrown together but more carefully. There's still plenty of sleazy guitar licks and scuzzy bass lines but the playing is tighter, a little more lacquered. It's the same throw in everything-but-the-kitchen-sink approach, but overall it feels like there's a steadier hand guiding the chaos.

The big difference between *Ill Communication* and *Check Your Head* is the quality of the rhymes. For the latest album, the Beastie Boys had stepped up their game in the lyrical department. No more rhyming "commercial" with "commercial" as they did on "Pass The Mic" from *Check Your Head*.

As with *Paul's Boutique*, New York is ever-present on *Ill Communication* as the city that the Beastie Boys are always yearning to return to. They drop names of old school New York rappers like K-Rob, Rammellzee, and Busy Bee, as well as the long-gone New York radio show the Zulu Beat. "New York City is the place that I feel at home in," MCA raps on "The Scoop."

Ill Communication's mingling of hip-hip, hardcore, and funk was a direct reflection of what the Beastie Boys experienced on the New York club scene of the early 1980s, a time when the Cold Crush Brothers released a single called "Punk Rock Rap," and Afrika Bambaataa's DJ sets mixed funk, punk, and electronic music such as the Yellow Magic Orchestra.

"It's really a New York thing," Yauch told writer Daniel Levine at the time of the album's release. "When we were growing up, clubs wouldn't only play rap or punk or funk—you'd go to

hear a hardcore band and they'd play James Brown on the P.A. between the sets."

Also evident on the album is MCA's growing social conscience. On "Sure Shot," he apologizes for the sexist lyrics of the Beastie Boys' early work: "I want to say a little something that's long overdue/The disrespect to women has got to be through/To all the mothers and sisters and the wives and friends/I want to offer my love and respect to the end." On "Bodhisattva Vow," he affirms his increasing interest in Buddhism when he raps through a heavy fog of distortion: "For the rest of my lifetimes and even beyond/I vow to do my best, to do no harm."

Yauch was also the driving force, quite literally, behind "Sabotage", the first single from the album, which along with the popular video that accompanied it, was a big factor in boosting the sales of *Ill Communication*. It was one of the first songs recorded for the album but completed only two

weeks before the album was due, and Yauch's propulsive fuzz bass and Ad-Rock's angry blowtorch vocals ("I'm Buddy Rich when I fly off the handle") gave the Beastie Boys their biggest hit since "(You Gotta) Fight For Your Right (To Party!)" and sent mosh pits crazy in 1994. A 2011 British survey said it was one of the top five songs most likely to cause drivers to speed up or become more aggressive.

The video to the song was directed by Spike Jonze and parodied 1970s crime shows like *The Streets of San Francisco* and *Starsky and Hutch*. It featured the Beastie Boys as fake-mustache-wearing detectives jumping on car hoods and climbing onto roofs, chasing down suspects. Yauch came up with the idea and initially wanted the Beastie Boys to grow real mustaches for the shoot but forgot that Diamond and Horovitz had trouble growing facial hair.

The video was nominated for best video at MTV's 1994 VMA awards and when it lost to "Everybody Hurts" by REM, Adam Yauch made a memorable appearance dressed in lederhosen as his alter ego Nathaniel Hornblower, the Swiss cheesemaker, screaming, "This is an outrage. This is a farce," disrupting Michael Stipe's acceptance speech, before being thrown off the stage by MTV security. Judging by the bemused look on Stipe's face, the REM singer wasn't warned about the prank in advance. The Beastie Boys more or less discovered Jonze, and the popularity of the "Sabotage" video provided a springboard that enabled Jonze to jump into directing full-length movies.

The next stop for the Beastie Boys was Lollapalooza, their first appearance on the traveling alternative music festival. Initially, the group was wary of agreeing to appear because the festival had developed a bad reputation for being disorganized. Also, there was the issue of fan safety and sexual assaults in the mosh pit. Eventually, they decided to join the festival—on a bill that also included Smashing Pumpkins, A Tribe Called Quest, and George Clinton—opened in Las Vegas on June 6, 1994 to 11,000 people in a half-empty stadium under a 101-degree desert sun. As the tour progressed, the crowds got bigger and the Beastie Boys ended up playing before a million people.

The Beastie Boys made sure that inserts were placed inside the official program with a list of do's and don'ts regarding mosh pit etiquette, such as: help people if they fall down, don't crowd surf, don't taunt security, don't grab women's breasts, and most of all "Don't Be A Knucklehead… save the macho bullshit for *American Gladiators* tryouts, tough guy."

The Beastie Boys also brought along a posse of Tibetan monks who opened each show by chanting on the main stage, which was flanked by two 70-foot Buddha statues. This was the first time many fans learned about Yauch's involvement with Buddhism and the Free Tibet movement. Lollapalooza would turn out to be a practice run for a project dear to Yauch's heart, the Tibetan Freedom Concerts, which were designed to raise public awareness about the inhumane treatment of Tibetans under Chinese rule and which would end up consuming much of his energy for the rest of the decade.

LEFT: Nathaniel Hornblower (aka MCA) plays b-ball backstage with the rest of the band, 1996.

OPPOSITE: Ad-Rock comes to rock the sureshot, onstage at the "disorganized" Lollapalooza festival, Las Vegas, 1994.

AD-ROCK

❝ I feel like we are honest. I feel like we are brave men. I feel we are erotic in ways, sexy—I mean, to us. You know, what's sexy to you might not be sexy to someone else. Hardened, creative certainly, sensitive. There are lot of different words I could throw out to describe us as a band. ❞ AD-ROCK

❝ I think every person has the ability to affect change... through our every thought, our every word, the way that we interact with other people. We are constantly affecting the world. ❞ AD-ROCK

OPPOSITE: Ad-Rock's infamous three finger ring bling is on display. Also worn by actor Elijah Wood in the "Fight For Your Right Revisted" music video, 1987.

ABOVE, RIGHT: Ad-Rock comes alive, onstage in L.A., California, 1987.

BELOW: Hours after attending the famous press conference with Run DMC, Ad-Rock rocks a New York crowd, 1987.

MUSICIANS WITH CONSCIENCE

In May 1994, the same month that *III Communication* was released, Adam Yauch started a nonprofit organization called the Milarepa Fund, named after an eleventh century Tibetan saint, Jetsun Milarepa, who sang songs to teach people about the path of nonviolence. The fund was intended to solve a dilemma that cropped up a year earlier: what should Yauch do with the royalties from the songs "Shambala" and "Bodhisattva Vow" from *III Communication,* which sampled Tibetan monks? He called his friend, human rights activist Erin Potts, and asked her what Tibetan organizations he should give the money to. She explained that the problem with donating to an outside organization is that you don't have any real control over how the group will spend the money. She suggested that she and Yauch set up their own nonprofit organization to disburse the funds to make the best use of the money. Thus, the Milarepa Fund was formed.

Potts, a campaigner for Tibetan freedom, first met Yauch during his 1991 snowboarding trip to Nepal. She was an exchange student from Connecticut College who majored in Tibetan studies and was spending her college year abroad in Katmandu. She wasn't a Buddhist, but on a previous trip to Nepal with her high school class, she had visited a Tibetan refugee camp and had vowed to help the Tibetan people in their struggle to free themselves from the brutal Chinese occupation of the small mountain country, which had been ongoing since 1950.

To say she was unimpressed with Yauch when she first met him would be an understatement. She hated the Beastie Boys, thought their music was vile and loathsome, but after she got to know Yauch she was won over by his obvious sincerity. "I had expectations of him being a jerk and he wasn't," she said.

On the 1994 Lollapalooza Tour, Potts sets up information tents at each stop to pass out literature explaining to Beastie Boys' fans about the dire situation in Tibet. She was also responsible for taking care of the Tibetan monks that the band had brought on tour with them. Yauch had arranged for one dollar from each ticket sold to go to the Milarepa Fund.

At some stops, when the Tibetan monks in saffron robes took to the stage blowing on long trumpets, they were met with catcalls and raised middle fingers by some concertgoers, but the reaction was mostly positive, if not too enthusiastic. Still, it was early days. Potts and Yauch's mission had only just begun.

"We were quickly learning about how to present Tibetan cultural and political issues at a concert," Yauch told blogger Mather Mockhawk. "We began to see what worked and what didn't. So by the time we finally pulled it together to do the first Tibetan Freedom Concert in San Francisco in June 1996, we had

some idea of what we were doing."

The first Tibetan Freedom Concert in the Polo Fields at San Francisco's Golden Gate Park—the site of 1967's famous Human Be-In that inaugurated "The Summer of Love"—was a mammoth undertaking. As Tibetan prayer flags fluttered in the breeze and attendees chowed down on Tibetan food, 20 bands played, including the Beastie Boys, Rage Against The Machine, the Smashing Pumpkins, and the Red Hot Chili Peppers. A

hundred thousand people attended over two days, making it the biggest benefit concert on U.S. soil since Live Aid. Working from Milarepa's headquarters, a cramped space in the North Beach neighborhood of San Francisco that was stuffed to the ceiling with Tibetan artifacts, Potts ferried bands to their hotels and then to the venue, as well as setting up a monastery tent for the monks and nuns who were there to educate concertgoers.

Despite the chilly weather (which recalled Mark Twain's

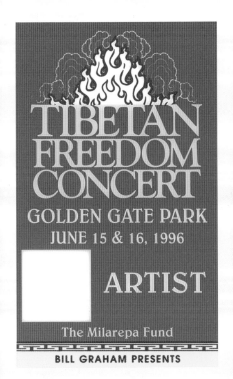

TIBETAN
FREEDOM
CONCERT

GOLDEN GATE PARK
JUNE 15 & 16, 1996

ARTIST

The Milarepa Fund

BILL GRAHAM PRESENTS

OPPOSITE: Björk supports The Milarepa Fund, with MCA, in San Francisco, 1996.

ABOVE: An Artist's AAA pass to Golden Gate Park, 1996.

RIGHT: The Beastie Boys take to the chilly San Fransican stage, performing at the Tibetan Freedom Concert, 1996.

famous quote: "The coldest winter I ever spent was a summer in San Francisco"), despite the recording truck that was meant to capture the event failing to turn up, and despite De La Soul being unable to take the stage because of equipment problems, the concert was a runaway success. The event raised over $800,000 for the Milarepa Fund, a good sum considering Yauch and Potts refused any commercial sponsorship. Students For A Free Tibet, an organization closely allied with the Milarepa Fund, was flooded with phone calls following the concert and saw a tenfold increase in chapters (from about 30 to 300) in the three months after the event. Yauch and Potts' efforts had succeeded in raising awareness about human rights abuses in Tibet with a generation that before the concert couldn't have found Tibet on a map. The momentum that the concert created, however, would prove difficult to maintain in the coming years.

The next Tibetan Freedom Concert took place in New York in June of the following year. Yauch and Potts initially wanted to take the event to the nation's capital to force politicians to take notice, but when that plan fell through, the duo hastily arranged

to stage the show at Downing Stadium on Randall's Island, a dump of a venue that held only half the capacity of the Polo Fields. The Saturday show was poorly attended but after MTV started to plug the event, the next day was a sellout. The lineup of bands was less stellar than the San Francisco concert, but the show did feature a rare performance by punk poetess Patti Smith, a solo acoustic set by Noel Gallagher from Oasis, and a short five-song blast from U2. The event raised about $250,000 for the Milarepa Fund, far less than the San Francisco concert.

The next Tibetan Freedom concert, held at Washington, D.C.'s RFK Stadium the following summer, even outshone San Francisco both for the number of attendees (120,000) and the money raised for the cause ($1.2 million) but the proceedings were marred by a lightning strike during jazz funkateer Herbie Hancock's set that sent 12 people to the hospital, nearly killing one woman. The announcement by REM's Michael Stipe that the first day's festivities had to be cut short because of the lightning strike was met with a chorus of boos and thrown water bottles.

If Saturday's events were marred by an act of God, Sunday's

proceedings were marred by human incompetence. Equipment glitches bedeviled acts throughout the day. REM's set was a garbled mess caused by a microphone that kept malfunctioning, though Michael Stipe's choice to wear a skirt onstage did provide a temporary moment of comic relief among the disgruntled crowd. The Beastie Boys tried to save the day with a blistering version of "Sabotage," which sent the mosh pit into a frenzy, but the audience was clearly not happy. However, 15–20,000 people did attend a protest on the Capitol lawn the next day, which was widely covered in the mainstream media, not a bad number for a political demonstration.

By the time of the fourth Tibetan Freedom Concert in 1999 at the Alpine Valley Theater in rural Wisconsin two hours' drive from Chicago, the goodwill among music-lovers that Yauch and Potts had built was clearly evaporating. Numbers were way down, only 31,000, and the event raised a fraction of what it did in Washington, D.C. A demonstration after the concert outside the Chinese consulate in Chicago attracted only 400 people. In part it was the ill-chosen location and the less

than stellar lineup (Run DMC hadn't had a hit in three years, Blondie in 15), but it was also that message fatigue had set in.. So did the events live up to Yauch and Potts' lofty aims? Did the concerts do anything to force the Chinese government to relent? Not according to the U.S. State Department who reported no change in the human rights situation in Tibet during this period.

Charles Aaron writing in *Spin* magazine summed up the cynic's case: "An event such as the Tibetan Freedom Concert, which rarely delineates between the Chinese citizenry and its vicious government, which patronizes the Tibetans as magically serene people, is going to give pause... especially since MTV is broadcasting it all like the feel-good event of the summer."

Yauch was undeterred by the criticism. Indeed he broadened his focus beyond Tibet when he took on President Bill Clinton for the retaliatory airstrikes against Sudan and Afghanistan, following the 1998 bombings of the U.S. embassies in Nairobi, Kenya, and Dar es Salaam, Tanzania, by Islamic terrorists that killed hundreds of people. In August 1998, at shows at both New York's Madison Square Garden and at New Jersey's Continental Arena, he was booed by fans when he characterized the U.S. response to the U.S. Embassy bombings as a form of racism against Muslims.

Then, at the 1998 VMA awards, while accepting the Michael Jackson Video Vanguard Award, he asked the cheering throng to bear with him for a moment while he spoke his mind. "I

think it was a real mistake that the U.S. chose to fire missiles into the Middle East, I think that was a huge mistake," he said. "It's very important that the United States starts to look at nonviolent means of resolving conflicts. Those bombings that took place in the Middle East, we thought it was a retaliation by the terrorists, and if we thought that what we did is retaliation, certainly we're going to find more retaliation from people in the Middle East, from terrorists specifically, I should say, because most Middle Eastern people are not terrorists."

Up to this point, it was the standard Buddhist boilerplate that violence begets more violence, but then he went further.

"Another thing America needs to think about is our racism— racism that comes from the United States toward Muslim people and toward Arabic people. And that's something that has to stop."

You didn't have to agree with everything he said to admire the bravery it took to make that statement in front of a national audience.

LEFT: MCA in a boiler suit, promoting his "boilerplate" beliefs, 1997

BELOW: MCA's MTV VMA acceptance speech showed the musician's passion for peace in the Middle East, 1998.

OPPOSITE: Onstage, on message, and on form, the band perform with energy and passion, live in the Netherlands, 1996.

ROOT DOWN

The Beastie Boys' new spiritual and political awareness wasn't the only thing that changed the trio, marriage did too. The first Beastie Boy to get hitched was Adam Horovitz in 1992. He wed Ione Skye, the actress best known for her role in the 1989 romantic comedy *Say Anything* as the object of John Cusack's famous boom-box serenade. Skye was dating Red Hot Chili Pepper's singer Anthony Kiedis when she met Horovitz during the making of *Paul's Boutique*.

Skye was then at the height of her fame, hot off the success of *Say Anything*. Horovitz was dating another actress Molly Ringwald. The two fell in love but they kept their affair a secret from their respective partners for months. Skye was reportedly sick of Kiedis being on the road all the time and she worried that Kiedis might lapse back into heroin addiction. Horovitz was more her age and he made her laugh, unlike the moody Kiedis. Further complicating things, Kiedis was friends with Horovitz. When Kiedis found out, he was fine with the situation and continued to be friends with Horovitz and Skye.

After the marriage, Horovitz and Skye moved into a house together in Laurel Canyon and, at first, they seemed like an ideal couple, according to friends of the Beastie Boys, but by 1995 they were separated, and they divorced in 1998. A few weeks after filing for divorce from her eight-year husband, Skye went on the *Howard Stern Show* and confessed that she was bisexual and was dating model Jenny Shimizu.

In a 2008 interview, she cited the same reason for the breakup of her marriage as she had for her split with Kiedis: "It wasn't fans or anything," said Skye. "I think I was mad that he spent all this time on the road." Horovitz remarried—to Bikini Kill singer, and feminist icon, Kathleen Hanna in 2006.

Mike D's marriage was more successful. In 1993, Diamond married filmmaker Tamra Davis. They were introduced by Delicious Vinyl's Matt Dike, who helped produce *Paul's Boutique*. Dike and Davis were college friends. Davis has produced a string of music videos for artists such as NWA, Depeche Mode, and Sonic Youth. She also directed the video for "Netty's Girl" from the "Pass The Mic" single.

Davis is probably best known for three comedies she directed in the 1990s, the hip-hop spoof *CB4*, the Adam Sandler vehicle *Billy Madison*, and the comedy *Half-Baked* with Dave Chappelle.

Davis put her career on hold to have two children with Diamond, Davis and Skyler. After her second child she realized that she wouldn't be returning to work as a full-time filmmaker any time soon, so she started the *Tamra Davis Cooking Show*. The web-show was filmed in the kitchen of Davis and Diamond's Malibu home and showed busy mothers like herself how to make healthy vegetarian food for their children.

Davis returned to film making in 2010 with *Jean-Michel Basquiat: The Radiant Child*, a documentary about the late artist Jean-Michel Basquiat who was the toast of downtown Manhattan in the 1980s before he died of a heroin overdose in 1988. The Beastie Boys weren't friends with Basquiat, but they certainly knew of each other since they hung out at many of the same nightclubs. Davis relied on her husband to provide the soundtrack to the movie, which includes such classics of the period as "Planet Rock" by Afrika Bambaataa and Soul Sonic Force and "Cavern" by Liquid Liquid. Diamond and Horovitz also provided original instrumentals for the documentary.

Instead of trashing hotel rooms, Diamond is more likely these days to redecorate them. When he and his wife moved to their new Brooklyn brownstone in 2012 after their second child was born, Diamond needed wallpaper for his new home. So he collaborated with New York designers Revolver to create Brooklyn Toile, a variation on French toile, a traditional wallpaper that depicts rustic scenes. But instead of shepherds and milkmaids, Brooklyn Toile depicts Hasidic Jews and The Notorious B.I.G.

The final Beastie Boy to make it to the altar was Adam Yauch, who on May 31, 1998 got hitched to Dechen Wangdu in an elaborate Tibetan wedding ceremony on Bleecker Street in New York's Greenwich Village.

Wangdu, a Tibetan-American activist, met Yauch at Harvard University, where they were both attending a speech by the Dalai Lama. Wangdu's favorite band Rancid—whose original vocalist ran off to a monastery to become a Buddhist monk—played the wedding.

The now-deceased Beastie Boys' tour manager, the Captain, told *Spin* magazine in 1998: "Her family got up and gave very regal, kind of Zen speeches. And then Yauch's family got up and embarrassed the fuck out of him." Yauch's uncle kept mentioning "(You Gotta) Fight For Your Right (To Party!)" in his toast, a record that Yauch had spent the last ten years trying to live down.

HELLO NASTY AND TO THE 5 BOROUGHS

Four years on from *Ill Communication* and the band drop *Hello Nasty*. A critical and commercial success, the album went to Number One in over a half-a-dozen countries. The band's next record, *To The 5 Boroughs*, saw the group return to, and fall back in love with, their hometown... New York City.

HELLO NASTY, 1998

#	Title	Time
1.	Super Disco Breakin'	2:07
2.	The Move	3:35
3.	Remote Control	2:58
4.	Song For The Man	3:13
5.	Just A Test	2:12
6.	Body Movin'	3:03
7.	Intergalactic	3:51
8.	Sneakin' Out The Hospital	2:45
9.	Putting Shame In Your Game	3:37
10.	Flowin' Prose	2:39
11.	And Me	2:52
12.	Three MC's And One DJ	2:50
13.	The Grasshopper Unit (Keep Movin')	3:01
14.	Song For Junior	3:49
15.	I Don't Know	3:00
16.	The Negotiation Limerick File	2:46
17.	Electrify	2:22
18.	Picture This	2:25
19.	Unite	3:31
20.	Dedication	2:32
21.	Dr. Lee, PhD	4:50
22.	Instant Death	3:22

TO THE 5 BOROUGHS, 2004

#	Title	Time
1.	Ch-Check It Out	3:12
2.	Right Right Now Now	2:46
3.	3 The Hard Way	2:48
4.	It Takes Time To Build	3:11
5.	Rhyme The Rhyme Well	2:47
6.	Triple Trouble	2:43
7.	Hey Fuck You	2:21
8.	Oh Word?	2:59
9.	That's It That's All	2:28
10.	All Lifestyles	2:33
11.	Shazam!	2:26
12.	An Open Letter to NYC	4:18
13.	Crawlspace	2:53
14.	The Brouhaha	2:13
15.	We Got The	2:27

OPPOSITE: The Boys' are photographed for Quincy Jones' *Vibe* magazine, L.A., California, 1998.

BACK IN NEW YORK
HELLO NASTY (1998) AND *TO THE 5 BOROUGHS* (2004)

One way to look at the Beastie Boys' post-Def Jam output is as a series of albums expressing their deep yearning to return to the mythical city of their youth. So much of *Paul's Boutique*, *Check Your Head,* and *III Communication* is firmly rooted in that period in the early 1980s when hip-hop was just starting to emerge from the ghetto and the carefree fun the Beastie Boys had smoking pot on rooftops, playing video games in arcades, and jumping from watching Black Flag at CBGBs to Afrika Bambaataa at the Roxy. What's striking about these albums is how many times New York is referenced yet Los Angeles, their home for eight years, is hardly ever mentioned. Chicago is name-checked more often than L.A. on *Paul's Boutique,* and Chicago is only mentioned once. What starts out as mere homesickness on *Paul's Boutique,* sounds more like a full-blown identity crisis by the time they get to *III Communication*. "It's like we're not really here," said Adam Horovitz when he was still living in Los Angeles.

I t's not as if they hated California. They enjoyed the easygoing lifestyle, but they could never shake that feeling that this wasn't really home, that they were in temporary exile somehow, that their true home was always calling them, and that one day soon they would make the move back. So when they finally made the decision to go back to New York in 1997, not only to record their fifth album, *Hello Nasty*, but to live there, it must have come as a blessed relief.

Released in August 1998, *Hello Nasty* saw the Beastie Boys jumping into their hot-tub time machine and traveling back to 1982, to land slap-bang in the middle of the dance floor at the Roxy nightclub where DJ Afrika Bambaataa was spinning on the wheels of steel and the Rock Steady Crew were spinning on their heads—an era when breakdancing and graffiti writing were just as important skills as deejaying or rapping, and rappers weren't called rappers but MCs who battled each other on the mic. The Beastie Boys were going back to their roots—not as a punk rock band as they did on *Check Your Head* and *Ill Communication*, but going back to their other set of roots as old school hip-hop aficionados who witnessed firsthand the legendary figures who created the music from the ground up. This was the album that the Beastie Boys would have made instead of *Licensed to Ill* if Rick Rubin had never wandered into their lives and made them listen to all that heavy metal nonsense.

Certainly, if you were young, adventurous and artistically inclined, and didn't mind the shitty living conditions and the always-present prospect that you might be stabbed or shot on your doorstep, downtown New York in the first half of the 1980s really was a paradise-on-earth for a certain type of cool cat. "It was home to a network of clubs, where an eclectic menu of alternative, punk, synth pop, new wave, rap, and underground records filled dance floors on a nightly basis," said former Def Jam executive Gary Harris. It was a period of cross-cultural collaboration when barriers between black music and white music were being dismantled, a time of freedom and creativity where the city's ruins provided a blank canvas on which you painted your own future and the future of the culture. Anything goes was the motto—and it frequently did.

"I'm the first to admit," Mike D once told *Spin*, "that we're totally dependent on a particular place and time."

It's the little things you remember, like the sawdust on the floor at one of the Beastie Boys' favorite hangouts, the after-hours club Save the Robots on Avenue B; the Spanish bodega just around the corner from where the photo for *Paul's Boutique* was shot, whose entire inventory was six cans of Goya beans that sat gathering dust on the shelf because the owner's real business was selling cocaine and heroin under the counter; that weird store in Greenwich Village whose permanent window display was a stuffed two-headed lamb and a Chinese typewriter; the clouds of steam that rose from the manholes that gave the city

❛ Time has healed our stupidity. We have learned and sincerely changed since the '80s. ❜❜

AD-ROCK

that film noir-ish *Taxi Driver* feel. In 1987, Mike D informed a visiting British journalist who asked about the steam that it was "alligator farts," a reference to the urban myth common then that colonies of alligators lived in the city's sewers.

"I love the early days," Adam Horovitz told *Rolling Stone* in 1998. "I guess everybody would like to be able to go back to the early days with all the knowledge you have now. And, of course, if I was in the early days, I'd be saying, 'I can't wait for the later days.' But you get nostalgic for that shit. There was nothing to do but hang out. It was good times. I was a lucky kid. I still definitely get to hang out, but it's not the same kind of hanging out. And, you know, I just get nostalgic. The changing times and shit. I get nostalgic for Atari."

The city that the Beastie Boys returned to was a very different place than the New York they had left less than ten years ago. By 1997, the

"I don't mean to brag, I don't mean to boast/But I'm intercontinental when I eat French toast," which is a homage to "Rapper's Delight" by the Sugarhill Gang ("I don't mean to brag, I don't mean to boast/But we like hot butter on our breakfast toast").

"Intergalactic," the first single from *Hello Nasty*, is straight-up electro-funk (the type of hip-hop music that Bambaataa pioneered at the Roxy and the Beastie Boys used to diss on the instructions of Rick Rubin) right down to the robotic voices and outer space imagery. "Intergalactic" also contains the funniest couplet on the record ("Keep on rapping cause that's my dream/Got an A from Moe Dee for sticking to themes"). Kool Moe Dee used to be part of the Treacherous Three who recorded for Sugar Hill Records. In 1987, after he went solo, he needled rival rappers by issuing report cards on their performances. He gave the Beastie Boys mostly Cs, the lowest ranking score of all the rappers he surveyed, but he did give them an A "for sticking to themes".

Hello Nasty reached Number One on the Billboard album charts in the United States and went on to win two Grammies for Best Alternative Music Album and Best Rap Performance by a Duo or Group. For most of the 1990s, the Beastie Boys seemed to be moving away from hip-hop to the point where it was debatable whether it was accurate to call them a rap group anymore. But as the group entered the new millennium, despite some of the filler tracks that clogged up the last half of the album and seemed to

process of gentrification was well under way. The East Village—the dynamo of creativity that lit up the whole of downtown during the 1980s—was starting to look like a cross between Restaurant Row and a bedroom community for Wall Street. Artists and musicians were fleeing downtown in droves because of spiraling rents. The wave of gentrification that swept downtown in the 1990s was still ongoing, but the signs were clearly on the wall. The old New York was being swept off the map block by block.

If the Beastie Boys couldn't turn back the tide of gentrification, they could at least recreate the city of their youth in their imagination along with the communal vibe that characterized hip-hop at the time before it became big business. That is exactly what they did on *Hello Nasty,* which is replete with obscure old-school references, both musically and lyrically.

The opening track, "Super Disco Breakin'" establishes the retro mood right up front with a sample of Run DMC's 1984 hit "Sucker MCs" as well as lyrical references to "money-making Manhattan" (a common phrase used in hip-hop records at the time) and the "Roland 808," the first programmable drum machine. This was introduced into hip-hop by the Japanese electronic group Yellow Magic Orchestra after Bambaataa began playing the trio's 1980 song "Riot In Lagos" at the Roxy. The Roland TR 808 subsequently became the rhythmical base of hip-hop during the following decade, including the first Beastie Boys record on Def Jam, "Rock Hard".

The next cut on the album, "The Move," not only featured a human beat box and a harpsichord interlude, it had Mike D rapping:

have been thrown in as an afterthought, the Beastie Boys had reestablished themselves not only as hip-hop heavyweights, but the real New Yorkers they always were.

Six years passed before the Beastie Boys' next album *To The 5 Boroughs*, in 2004. When the group announced that the album was going to be a tribute to New York, it seemed redundant. Aren't all Beastie Boys albums tributes to New York in one way or another? But this was different. If *Hello Nasty* was an album about New York as it was, *To The 5 Boroughs* was about New York as it is, especially after the 9/11 attack on the World Trade Center.

The centerpiece of the album is "An Open Letter To NYC" on which Mike D raps, "Dear New York, I know a lot has changed/Two towers down but you're still in the game," was a tribute to the people of New York and its cultural diversity. Set to a sample of the Dead Boys' "Sonic Reducer," on the rousing chorus, the group rapped in unison: "Brooklyn, Bronx, Queens, and Staten/From the Battery to the top of Manhattan/Asian, Middle-Eastern, and Latin/Black, White, New York you make it happen."

The Beastie Boys' trademark sense of humor is still here ("I've got billions and billions of rhymes to flex/I've got more rhymes than Carl Sagan's got turtlenecks" on "Hey, Fuck You") but the album reflects the group's increasing commitment to political awareness. MCA smacks down President George W. Bush a number of times on the album both for the War on Terror ("Is the U.S. gonna keep breaking necks?/Maybe it's time we impeach Tex," on "Time To Build") and for his lack of concern for the environment ("We've got a president we didn't elect/The Kyoto Treaty he decided to neglect," from the same song).

Perhaps the most surprising development during this period was the way that Ad-Rock was becoming increasingly vocal, both as a feminist and an advocate for gay rights. He admonished male fans for groping women in mosh pits and apologized for the band's rampant homophobia during their *Licensed to Ill* period in a letter to *Time Out New York*. "I would like to formally apologize to the entire gay and lesbian community for the shitty and ignorant things we said on our first record," Horovitz wrote. "There are no excuses. But time has healed our stupidity. We have learned and sincerely changed since the '80s. We hope that you'll accept this long overdue apology."

OPPOSITE, ABOVE: Back to their beast: performing in sync at the MTV Latin Video Music Awards, 2004.

BELOW: Road-testing the "Rhyme and Reason" tour, 2000.

THIS PAGE: The band backstage, New York, 2001: having recently returned to their home city, the band's new material was instantly influenced by the immediate aftereffects of 9/11.

THREE BROTHERS

The Beastie Boys were never the most prolific group in the world but the six-year gap between *Hello Nasty* and *To the 5 Boroughs* was a long time even by their standards, so to mollify fans, three years later, the Beastie Boys released an all-instrumental album. *The Mix-Up*, which debuted on June 26, 2007, was an interesting idea in theory but it was hardly classic Beastie Boys. When the instrumentals were just interludes between the songs, as on *Ill Communication* and *Hello Nasty,* they worked fine because the tracks created a breathing space between the more frenetic cuts, but a whole album of listening to them noodling away wasn't exactly essential listening. By this point, the Beastie Boys had become competent musicians. Even so, they weren't Booker T. and the MGs or The Meters.

The cheesy psychedelia of "14th St. Break" sounded like something from the scene in the Clint Eastwood movie *Coogan's Bluff* when he visited a hippie nightclub called the Pigeon Toed Orange Peel. Hanging out with the legendary dubmeister Lee "Scratch" Perry had obviously influenced the group, especially on the reggae-inflected tracks like "The Gala Event," and "Electric Worm", but compared to the great man himself or other dub artists like Augustus Pablo, King Tubby, or the Mad Professor, this was second-rate material. And did we really need another soundtrack to the blaxploitation movie that had been playing on an endless loop inside the Beastie Boys' heads since *Paul's Boutique* ("Freaky Hijiki," "The Melee," "Biscuits and Butter")?

Surprisingly, *The Mix-Up* won a Grammy for Best Pop Instrumental Album, the group's third. Having ignored their best work (*Paul's Boutique, Check Your Head, Ill Communication,* and, yes, *Licensed to Ill*), the National Academy of Recording Arts and Sciences was now so enamored of the Beastie Boys, one suspects that the organizers' would have given them a Grammy if they'd released an album of white noise.

Far more intriguing was the film project that Adam Yauch cooked up, the 2006 concert movie *Awesome I Fuckin' Shot That!*. The first movie released by Oscilloscope Laboratories, the independent film company founded by Yauch, it was created by handing out camcorders to 50 audience members at the Beastie Boys' October 2004 show at Madison Square Garden. Admittedly, the resulting movie was a bit of a chaotic mess, however it did serve to illustrate the extraordinary bond between the group and their fans, the nearest equivalent of which was the Grateful Dead and their followers.

Yauch, Horovitz, and Diamond entered New York's Oscilloscope Laboratories in 2008 to make their eighth album. Oscilloscope, as well as being a film company, also housed a

recording studio. Yauch had fitted out the studio with vintage analog equipment, including a Neve mixing board—the same console that the early Def Jam records were recorded on—which audiophiles claim gives a much warmer and more individual sound than digital mixing boards, which tend to flatten out music and make everything sound the same. After two clean-sounding, relatively sparse hip-hop albums —*Hey Nasty* and *To The 5 Boroughs*—the idea was to return to the sonic anarchy of *Check Your Head* and *Ill Communication*. Also, the Beastie Boys wanted to bring back the punk rock energy missing from both *Hello Nasty* and *To The 5 Boroughs*. By early 2009, the Beastie Boys had so much material, they decided to release two albums, *Hot Sauce Committee Part One* and *Hot Sauce Committee Part Two*.

News of the new record first leaked in February at the Independent Spirit Awards in Los Angeles, when Adam Yauch told reporters about a "bizzare" and "weird" new album that would be the Beastie Boys' most experimental effort to date. He said the group was in the process of putting the finishing touches to the album and it should be out by the end of the year.

The Beastie Boys officially announced in June that *Hot Sauce Committee Part One*—their first vocal album in five years—would be released on September 15 and featured guest spots by the singer Santigold and the rapper Nas. Nas had recently joined the Beastie Boys onstage at the Bonnaroo music festival to debut a song from the album "Too Many Rappers," which contained the refrain: "Too many rappers and not enough MCs," indicating that the members of the Beastie Boys were unhappy with the state of contemporary hip-hop. The group had also been confirmed as headliners at three other U.S. music festivals—Lollapalooza, Outside Lands, and Austin City Limits.

All plans for the Beastie Boys' big comeback were put on indefinite hold after a shocking announcement the following month. On July

20, 2009, Adam Yauch posted a video to the Beastie Boys official website in which he announced that doctors had just diagnosed him with lymphatic cancer. What Yauch had initially thought was simply a case of swollen glands had turned out to be something far more serious. Flanked by a bearded Adam Horovitz, a relaxed, deceptively healthy-looking Yauch appeared in good spirits, even laughing at some points in the video, when he told Beastie Boys fans "We're going to have to cancel some of our shows and push back our record release," while he underwent surgery.

In early August, Yauch updated his fans about the operation with an email. The email's subject line—"What I did over my summer vacation"—showed he hadn't lost his sense of humor. He seemed upbeat when he wrote that the surgery had gone well and, while he was feeling a little stiff, he was "rapidly recovering… so things are moving along." In a follow-up email to fans three months later, Yauch wrote that, after a visit to India, where he met the Dalai Lama and underwent a healing ceremony at a Buddhist nunnery, he was "taking Tibetan medicine and at the recommendation of the Tibetan doctors I've been eating a vegan/organic diet." He ended on a positive note, "I'm feeling healthy, strong and hopeful that I've beaten this thing, but of course time will tell."

Yauch was also in good enough health to direct a hilariously surreal star-studded 30 minute short film, "Fight for Your Right Revisited." The short starts immediately after the events of the group's 1987 video "(You Gotta) Fight For Your Right (To Party!)" and starred Danny McBride playing MCA, Elijah Wood as Ad-Rock, and Seth Rogan as Mike D. In the movie, the Beastie Boys crawl out of the wreckage of an apartment they've just trashed with a sledgehammer only to be confronted by the apartment's owners (Stanley Tucci and Susan Sarandon). They then burglarize a bodega, get stabbed by Chloe Sevigny, drop acid with groupies, and finally get into a breakdancing competition with a future version of the Beastie Boys (played by Will Ferrell, Jack Black and John C. Reilly) who have traveled back in time in a DeLorean car, as in *Back To The Future*. The film ends with the young and old Beastie Boys getting into a pissing match, literally peeing on each other, before being carted off in a paddy wagon.

The confusingly titled *Hot Sauce Committee Part Two* finally hit the stores nearly two years later than planned. *Hot Sauce Committee Part Two*, which was released on April 27, 2011, was supposed to be the title of the follow-up to *Part One*. *Part Two*, however, seemed to be a slightly rejigged version of Part One and it was unclear if a second album would ever be released. The album debuted at Number Two on the *Billboard* album chart and *Hot Sauce Committee Part Two* turned out to be just as experimental as Yauch had predicted.

The album is an astonishing achievement on so many levels: as sonically sophisticated as *Paul's Boutique*, as deliciously unhinged as *Check Your Head*, as artfully chaotic as *Ill Communication*, and —even though they make fun of their advancing years on "Too Many Rappers" ("Just look at me/

Grandpa been rapping since '83") —just as energetic as on *Licensed to Ill*. Instead of settling into a comfortable, middle-aged groove, coasting along on their previous achievements, the Beastie Boys obviously decided to go for broke this time and set the musical blender on blast to see how far they could stretch their sound until it collapsed under its own weight, which it surprisingly never does. It's a high-wire balancing act that a band half their age would be scared to try but the Beastie Boys show themselves to be absolutely fearless. What comes across most of all on *Hot Sauce Committee Part Two* is that here is a group that is still in love with sound for sound's sake, a band with a restless creative spirit that is determined to explore the outer limits of what we mean by music.

The reverb-heavy "Don't Play No Game That I Can't Win," which features Santigold's lilting vocals floating across an undulating dub landscape, where the Beastie Boys' voices drift in and out of the mix like ghostly Doppler effects, is simply gorgeous, a word I thought would never apply to a Beastie Boys song. Even on the more stripped-down hardcore hip-hop songs such as "Make Some Noise," "Here's A Little Something For Ya," and "Too Many Rappers" (where the trio share the microphone with Brooklyn rapper Nas), the Beastie Boys constantly come up with new ways to make familiar sounds unfamiliar. At a time when hip-hop as a genre had wandered down a musical cul-de-sac it seemed incapable of finding its way out of, the group keeps finding extra

dimensions to explore, constantly expanding their sound without losing sight of the basics.

On the cranked-up-really-high punk rock song "Lee Majors Come Again", the Beastie Boys manage to figure out how to loosen the musical straitjacket that hardcore punk had decades ago become, to make something that sounds fresh and exciting, even strangely light and airy. There's tons of distortion on the album but it doesn't sound like Slayer (or even *Check Your Head*) because it's aesthetically pleasing distortion that never descends into cacophony, thanks in no small part to the wigged-out genius of the album's remixer, the crazy Frenchman Philippe Zdar.

And as for the rapping, the Beastie Boys are still as witty as ever, whether rhyming basketball player John Salley with *Vogue* editor André Leon Talley ("Here's A Little Something For Ya") or turning the party manifesto of "(You Gotta) Fight For Your Right (To Party!)" on "Make Some Noise" into a political manifesto: "You gotta party for your motherfuckin' right to fight." Ad-Rock probably has the funniest line: "Can't tell me nothing, can't tell me nada/Don't quote me now because I'm doing the Lambada" ("Make Some Noise"). MCA has never sounded better, his gravelly voice imbued with a new gravitas as an elder statesman of hip-hop who schools the young 'uns: "My rhymes, they age like wine as I get older." Even the throwaway instrumental, the irresistibly funky "Multilateral Nuclear Disarmament" is more compelling than anything on *The Mix-Up*.

In short, *Hot Sauce Committee Part Two* ranks up there with *Paul's Boutique* as a candidate for the group's best album, and, as it would soon turn out, an album that stands as a monumental epitaph to a man of monumental talent.

So it seemed fitting that the following April, the Beastie Boys were inducted into the Rock and Roll Hall of Fame. Adam Yauch was too unwell to attend but he did send a letter, which Adam Horovitz read to the audience. "I'd like to dedicate this to my brothers Adam and Mike. They walked the globe with me. It's also for anyone who has ever been touched by our band. This induction is as much ours as it is yours."

At 9am on May 4, 2012, after a nearly three-year battle with cancer, Yauch died at the New York-Presbyterian Hospital in Manhattan. His wife Dechen Wangdu and their 13-year-old daughter Tenzin were by his side. He was 47.

"He was a very courageous person," his mother Frances, told *The New York Times*. "He was hopeful to the very end."

To sum up the life and career of Adam Yauch in a few simple rules to live by: don't forget your roots; never sell out because you'll come to regret it; always keep on pushing creatively; and if you behave like a dickhead, and who doesn't at some point in their life, have the humility to apologize.

Adam Yauch set an example for the rest of us to follow.

LEFT: Promoting and performing *Hot Sauce Committee Part Two*, 2008.

ABOVE: MCA and the boys' perform at Exit Music Festival, Novi Sad, Serbia, 2007.

OPPOSITE: 2011: news of MCA's "recovery" are "exaggerated" in the press. "Time will tell," the singer announces.

"To sum up the life and career of Adam Yauch in a few simple rules to live by: don't forget your roots; never sell out because you'll come to regret it; always keep on pushing creatively; and if you behave like a dickhead, and who doesn't at some point in their life, have the humility to apologize."

"I'm glad to know that all the love Yauch has put out in the world is coming right back at him." AD-ROCK

"The Beastie Boys were one of a kind! And so was Adam! They were all an important part of my musical history and integral to the musical revolution that was happening at the time." MADONNA

"Adam was incredibly sweet and most sensitive artist who I loved dearly and was always inspired by his work. He will be missed by all of us." RUSSELL SIMMONS

"It's impossible to measure the influence Adam Yauch and the Beastie Boys have had on hip-hop culture as a whole, and on rock and roll in general. Adam's legacy here at Def Jam is nothing short of iconic—he was one of the pioneering artists of this great label and family." JOIE MANDA, PRESIDENT, DEF JAM RECORDINGS

ABOVE: No sleep till Brooklyn: Poignant street tributes to MCA, New York, 2012.

OPPOSITE: The band perform at the esteemed Bonnaroo Festival, Manchester, Tennessee, 2009. Ad-Rock, for once, takes a seat.

CODA: WHAT NEXT FOR THE BEASTIE BOYS?

In the wake of Yauch's death, the surviving members of the Beastie Boys, Adam Horovitz and Mike Diamond, chose mainly to grieve in private, though they did release statements to fans on their respective Facebook pages. Mike D wrote, "I miss Adam so much. He really served as a great example for myself and so many of what determination, faith, focus, and humility coupled with a sense of humor can accomplish. The world is in need of many more like him. We love you Adam."

Horovitz expressed similar sentiments on his Facebook page. "I wanna say thank you to all our friends and family (which are kinda one and the same) for all the love and support. I'm glad to know that all the love that Yauch has put out in the world is coming right back at him."

Two weeks after Yauch's death, Horovitz was spotted in Manhattan's Union Square at a low-key gathering of fans who had come to pay their respects as part of "MCA Day." Mike D spent Thanksgiving handing out food to victims of Hurricane Sandy in Far Rockaway, a coastal community in New York that was particularly hard-hit by the storm.

As devastated as they were by their friend's death, they haven't ruled out the possibility that the Beastie Boys may continue in one form or another, but they have yet to make a decision.

BELOW: The white stuff: The Beastie Boys' iconic look, 1987.
OPPOSITE: Growing old and (almost) grown up, 2006.

SKILLS TO PAY THE BILLS: A TIMELINE

In a career spanning over 30 years, the Beastie Boys have been integral to many iconic and landmark moments in music history, and have not only significantly altered the music industry, but also inspired and entertained millions of fans who have grown up with the band and their era-defining, and often genre-bending, fusion of hip-hop, rap, rock, punk, and pop.

1981

Mike Diamond and Adam Yauch, along with John Berry and Kate Schellenbach, start out as a punk rock band called the Beastie Boys —a name that "was the stupidest thing we could think of," claims Mike D.

1984

Def Jam debuts its first release, "It's Yours," by T La Rock and Jazzy Jeff. It's a hit.

The Beastie Boys sign to Def Jam and perform at black rap clubs and, eventually, are asked to open for Madonna on her infamous "Like A Virgin" tour.

1986

Licensed to Ill is released and sells eight million copies. The band headline their own world tour.

1989

Despite disputes with Def Jam, Paul's Boutique is released.

1992

Check Your Head is released.

1994

The band release the EP Some Old Bullshit in February.

May: MCA starts the nonprofit organisation, Milarepa Fund.

The single "Sabotage" is released in January 1994, along with the music video, directed by Spike Jonze. The video is nominated in five categories at the MTV Music Video Awards in September. The band also drops Ill Communication in May 1994 and it goes to Number One in the U.S. for one week.

Nathaniel Hornblower (aka MCA) mock-protests at the MTV Awards, for losing out in "Best Video" to R.E.M's "Everybody Hurts."

1982

The four members release the 7-inch EP Poly Wog Stew, on Rat Cage Records and, later in the year, disband.

1985

The band join the bill with Run-DMC and LL Cool J, and the shows, in the U.S. and U.K., are aptly named the "Raising Hell" tour.

1987

In May, Ad-Rock is arrested on assault charges in Liverpool, England, after a beer can hits a fan—deflected off a baseball bat swing—at the prestigious Royal Court Theatre. He is later found not guilty.

The band and Rick Rubin part company over royalty disputes.

1995

"Sabotage" is nominated for a Grammy, Best Hard Rock Performance.

1996

In June, the band organizes and performs at the Tibetan Freedom Concert in San Francisco.

1983

Ad-Rock joins Mike Diamond and Adam Yauch as guitarist and the trio release the 12-inch EP Cooky Puss.

British Airways used a portion of the song "Beastie Revolution" in a TV advertisement without the band's permission. The group receive a $40,000 settlement.

Rick Rubin is hired as DJ, and encourages the band to grab their crotches "like real rappers do".

1993

The band are nominated for their first Grammy Award for Best Rap Performance by a Duo or Group for Check Your Head.

Mike D marries movie director Tamra Davies.

1997

The Rock and Roll Hall of Fame induct "(You Gotta) Fight For Your Right (To Party!)" as one of the 500 Songs That Shaped Rock And Roll.

1998

Hello Nasty is released and "Intergalactic" hits the Top 40 in the U.S., and many European countries. Mixmaster Mike joins the band.

August: The band asks fellow performers at the Reading Festival, U.K., The Prodigy not to perform "Smack My Bitch Up." The band believes the song "clearly promotes violence against woman." The Prodigy perform the song, regardless.

The band are named *Rolling Stone's* Artist of the Year.

MCA marries Dechen Wangdu.

2004

March: *To The 5 Boroughs* is released.

2006

Ad-Rock marries Kathleen Hanna.

The MCA-directed concert movie *Awesome I Fuckin' Shot That!* is released, a project that involved handing out 50 camcorders to 50 audience members at the band's sellout show at Madison Square Garden, 2004.

2007

The Beastie Boys perform four songs at the Live Earth concert at Wembley Stadium, London, organized by Al Gore to raise awareness concerning the climate crisis.

2012

The Beastie Boys are inducted into the Rock and Roll Hall of Fame, in April. MCA is too ill to attend.

May 4: At 9am, Adam Yauch dies at the age of 47, after a three-year battle with cancer.

1999

February: The band wins two Grammy Awards for Best Alternative Performance, and Best Rap Performance.

December: The band issues a letter to *Time Out* magazine apologizing for their early behavior and attitudes toward the gay community.

2003

The band post the anti-George W. Bush track "In A World Gone Mad" to their website. The song attacks the Bush Administration over the war in Iraq.

A federal judge ruled that the Beastie Boys use of a six-second-flute sample from James Newton's "Choir" in their song "Pass The Mic" did not constitute copyright infringement. This ruling helped paved the way for hip-hop's increasingly common use of samples. This was also a landmark decision in the music industry's ongoing, and complex, relationship with intellectual property law.

2009

July 20, MCA posts a video to the official Beastie Boys' website announcing that doctors had just diagnosed him with lymphatic cancer.

2013

Mike D releases a new, ten-minute-long song, "Humberto vs. the New Reactionaries," a track commissioned by fashion house Kenzo, for their Spring/Summer 2014 show.

Ad-Rock and Mike D sign a deal to release the long-awaited, and official, Beastie Boys memoir, due in 2015.

The Beastie Boys threaten toy company GoldieBlox with a lawsuit after a commercial goes viral that uses a rewritten working of the band's "Girls" into a "powerful anthem for teenage girls." "In no event may my image or name or any music or any artistic property created by me be used for advertising purposes," MCA's will states. The toy company claim "fair use."

2000

Mike D sustains a shoulder injury while cycling. The accident ends up canceling the proposed "Rhyme and Reason" tour with Rage Against The Machine.

2011

MCA writes and directs the comedic video to the song "Fight For Your Right Revisited," to commemorate the 25th anniversary of "(You Gotta) Fight For Your Right (To Party!)". The video accompanies the release of the single "Make Some Noise" and stars many Hollywood actors.

ALRIGHT HEAR THIS: DISCOGRAPHY

The following is a chronological listing of the complete Beastie Boys EPs, singles, albums, compilations, anthologies, and video releases, as officially produced by the band and distributed by their record labels since 1982.

SINGLES

1983 "Cooky Puss," Rat Cage Records
1985 "Rock Hard," Def Jam Recordings
1985 "She's On It," Def Jam Recordings
1986 "Hold It Now, Hit It," CBS/Def Jam Recordings
1986 "The New Style," Def Jam Recordings
1986 "Paul Revere," Def Jam Recordings
1987 "Brass Monkey", CBS Records/Def Jam Recordings
1987 "(You Gotta) Fight For Your Right (To Party!)" CBS Records/Def Jam Recordings
1987 "No Sleep Till Brooklyn," CBS Records/ Def Jam Recordings
1987 "Girls," CBS Records/Def Jam Recordings
1989 "Hey Ladies," Capitol Records
1989 "An Exciting Evening At Home With Shadrach, Meshach and Abednego." Capitol Records
1992 "Pass The Mic," Capitol Records
1992 "So What'cha Want," Capitol Records
1992 "Jimmy James," Capitol Records
1992 "Gratitude," Capitol Records
1992 "Professor Booty," Capitol Records
1994 "Sabotage," Grand Royal Records
1994 "Get It Together," Grand Royal Records
1994 "Sure Shot," Grand Royal Records
1998 "Intergalactic," Capitol Records
1998 "Body Movin'," Grand Royal Records/ Columbia Records
1998 "The Negotiation Limerick File," Capitol Records
1999 "Remote Control / Three MCs And One DJ," Grand Royal Records/Capitol Records
1999 "Alive," Capitol Records
2004 "Ch-Check It Out," Capitol Records
2004 "Triple Trouble," EMI Records

2004 "Right Right Now Now," EMI Records
2004 'Now Get Busy," Grand Royal Records/ Capitol Records
2005 "An Open Letter To NYC," Capitol Records
2007 "The Electric Worm," Capitol Records
2009 "Lee Majors Come Again," Capitol Records
2009 "Too Many Rappers (featuring Nas)," Capitol Records
2011 "Make Some Noise," Capitol Records
2011 "Don't Play No Game I Can't Win (featuring Santigold)," Capitol Records

EPS

1982 *Polly Wog Stew*, Rat Cage Records
1994 *Pretzel Nugget*, Capitol Records/Grand Royal Records
1995 *Root Down*, Capitol Records/EMI Records
1995 *Aglio e Olio*, Capitol Records/Grand Royal Records
1998 *Nasty Bits*, Capitol Records
1999 *Scientists of Sound—The Blow Up Factor Vol. 1*, Capitol Records/Grand Royal Records
2008 *The Mix-Up Bonus Tracks*, Capitol Records

ALBUMS

1986 *Licensed to Ill*, Def Jam Recordings
1989 *Paul's Boutique*, Capitol Recordings/EMI Records
1992 *Check Your Head*, Capitol Recordings/EMI Records
1994 *Ill Communication*, Capitol Records/EMI Records/ Grand Royal Records
1998 *Hello Nasty*, Capitol Records/EMI Records
2004 *To The 5 Boroughs*, Capitol Records/EMI Records

2007 *The Mix-Up*, Capitol Records/EMI Records
2010 *Hot Sauce Committee Part Two*, Capitol Records/ EMI Records

COMPILATIONS

1994 *Hip Hop Sampler* (demos), Capitol Records
1994 *Some Old Bullshit*, Capitol Records/EMI Records/ Grand Royal Records
1994 *Tour Shot!*, Generic/EMI Records/Grand Royal Records
1996 *In Sound From Way Out!*, Capitol Records/EMI Records/ Grand Royal Records
1999 *Anthology: The Sounds of Science*, Capitol Records/ EMI Records/Grand Royal Records
2005 *Solid Gold Hits*, Capitol Records/EMI Records/ Parlophone

VIDEO ALBUMS

Beastie Boys, 1987, CBS Records
The Skills To Pay The Bills, 1992, Capitol Records
Sabotage, 1994, Capitol Records
Beastie Boys Video Anthology, 2000, The Criterion Collection, Capitol Records
Awesome; I Fuckin' Shot That!, 2006, Velocity, Think Film, Lionsgate

---

OPPOSITE: The fans' show their appreciation for the band, 1987.
NEXT PAGE: Performing at the KROQ Weenie Roast, L.A., California, 2004.

INDEX

"A Year And A Day" 46–7
A7 13
Aaron, Charles 70
AC/DC 27
Adler, Bill 27, 31, 33
"All Lifetsyles" 75
"Alone Again" 47, 55
"Alright Hear This" 61
"An Open Letter To NYC" 75, 79
"And Me" 75
"Ask For Janice" 35
Awesome I Fuckin' Shot That 80, 89
"B-Boy Bouillabaisse 35, 46
"B-Boys Makin' With The Freak Freak" 61
Bad Brains 12, 134
Bak, Sunny 26
Bambaataa, Afrika 11, 14, 63, 72, 76
"Beastie Revolution" 17, 88
Berman, David 36, 37, 39, 41, 48
Berry, John 13, 14, 88
"Biscuits And Butter" 80
Biz Markie 47, 55–6
"Biz vs. The Nuge, The" 51, 56
Blue, Ruza 14
"Blue Nun, The" 51
"Bobo On The Corner" 61
"Bodhisattva Vow" 61, 63, 68
"Body Movin'" 75
"Brass Monkey" 25
Brooklyn 31
"Brouhaha, The" 75
Cabasa, Lisa Ann 41
Caldato Jr., Mario 41, 55
Capitol Records 33, 36, 37, 39, 41, 45, 47, 48, 53–4, 5
"Car Thief" 35, 39, 46
Carr, Tim 36, 39
Castor, Jimmy 32
"Ch-Check It Out" 75
Check Your Head 11, 48, 51–7, 62, 63, 76, 81, 88
Christgau, Robert 29, 47
Chuck D 45, 89
Clash 38
Clash, The 8, 12, 13
Columbia Records 26, 32
"Cooky Puss" 14, 88
"Crawlspace" 75

Daily Mirror 8, 31
Danceteria 18, 20, 26
Davis, Miles 47
Davis, Stephen 30
Davis, Tamra 72, 88
De La Soul 47
"Dedication" 75
Def Jam 8, 11, 14, 16, 17, 20, 32, 33, 36, 38, 39, 41, 45, 47, 48, 54, 88
Delicious Vinyl 38
DeMann, Freddie 20
Diamond, Harold 12
Diamond, Hester 12
Dike, Matt 38, 39, 44, 72
DJ Hurricane 27, 30
"Do It" 61
"Don't Play No Game That I Can't Win" 82
Dr Dre 27
"Dr Lee, PhD" 75
Dust Brothers 38, 41, 46, 47, 54, 55
"Dust Joint" 39
"Egg Man" 35
"ElectricWorm" 80
"Electrify" 75
Enter the Dragon 38
Epic 19
Eric B 47
"Eugene's Lament" 61
"59 Chrystie Street" 17, 46
"Fight For Your Right Revisited" 81, 89
"Finger Lickin' Good" 51, 52, 54
"5-Piece Chicken Dinner" 35
Fleetwood, Amy 41
Flophouse Society Orchestra, The 31
"Flowin' Prose" 75
"Flute Loop" 61
"14th St. Break" 80
"Freaky Hijiki" 80
"Full Clout" 38–9
"Funky Boss" 51, 52
"Futterman's Rule" 61
"Gala Event, The" 80
"Get It Together" 61
"Girls" 25
Gore, Tipper 27
Grand Royal 58–9

Grashof, Alex 41
Grashof, Caroline 41
"Grasshopper Unit, The (Keep Movin')" 75
"Gratitude" 51
"Groove Holmes" 51
Guccione Jr., Bob 27, 29
Hammer of the Gods (Davis) 30
Handelman, David 47
Hanna, Kathleen 72, 89
Harris, Gary 77
"Heart Atttack Man" 61
Hello Nasty 75, 76–9, 89
"Here's A Little Something For You" 82
"Hey Fuck You" 75
"Hey Ladies" 35, 41, 47
"Hey Leroy" 32
"High Plains Drifter" 35, 41
Hill, Benny 8
"Hold It Now, Hit It" 25, 27, 29, 32, 33
Horovitz, Doris 12, 29
Horovitz, Israel 12
Hose 14
Hot Sauce Committee Part One 80
Hot Sauce Committee Part Two 11, 80–2
"Humberto vs. The New Reactionaries" 89
"I Don't Know" 75
"I Need A Beat" 17
Ill Communication 11, 61–4, 68, 76, 81, 88
"I'm Down" 29, 45
Imperial Knights of Schism 13
"In 3's" 51
"In A World Gone Mad" 89
In Search of Manny 58
"Instant Death" 75
"Intergalactic" 75, 78, 89
It Takes A Nation Of Millions To Hold Us Back 41, 47
"It Takes Time To Build" 75
"It's Yours" 16, 17, 88
Jackson, Michael 29
Jagger, Karis 41
Jeff, Jazzy 16
"Jimmy James" 51, 52
"Johnny Ryall" 35
"Just A Test" 75

Kiedis, Anthony 41, 72
King, Kerry 32, 44
Kitchen, The 14
Kool Moe Dee 78
Krush Kroove 20, 32
LA Times 17, 57
LA Weekly 41
"Lee Majors Come Again" 82
Leitch, Donovan 41
Leland, John 47
LeRoy, Dan 38, 39
Levine, Daniel 63
Licensed to Ill 8, 17, 25, 26, 29, 32, 33, 36, 37, 41, 45, 46, 47, 48, 54, 56, 62, 79, 88
"Lighten Up" 51
Live At Max's Kansas City 13
"Live At P.J.'s" 51
LL Cool J. 17, 26, 88
"Looking Down The Barrel Of A Gun" 35, 56
Lost Angels 31
Love, American Style 47
Luscious Jackson 56, 58
Madonna 20, 85, 88
"Maestro, The" 51, 53
"Make Some Noise" 82, 89
Manda, Joie 85
"Mark On The Bus" 51
Max's Kansas City 13
McLaren, Malcolm 14, 32
"Melee, The" 80
Melody Maker 8, 29
Milgrim, Hale 48, 53–4
Milarepa Fund 68, 69, 88
Mix-Up, The 11, 80, 82
Moore, Rudy Ray 47
Moore, Thurston 14
"Move, The" 75, 78
"Multilateral Nuclear Disarmanent" 82
Namasté 51, 53
Nas 80, 82
"Negotiation Limerick File, The" 75
"New Style, The" 25
New York 14, 48
Nishita, Mark Ramos (Money Mark) 41, 52, 54–5
"No Sleep Till Brooklyn" 25, 29, 31
"Oh Word?" 75

O'Sullivan, Gilbert 47
Parsons, Dave 13, 14
"Pass The Mic" 51, 52, 57, 62, 63, 89
"Paul Revere" 25
Paul's Boutique 17, 35–41, 44-8, 54, 55, 56, 57, 76, 77, 81, 82, 88
"Picture This" 75
Playboy 26, 30, 47
Polly Wog Stew 14, 88
"Posse In Effect" 25
Potts, Erin 68–9, 70
"POW!" 51
"Professor Booty" 51
Public Enemy 41, 47
"Putting Shame In Your Game" 75
Radio 17, 26
Raising Hell tour 27
"Rapper's Delight" 13
Rat Cage 13, 14
"Remote Control" 75
"Rhyme The Rhyme Well" 75
"Rhymin' & Stealin'" 25
"Ricky's Theme" 61
"Right Right Now Now" 75
Ringwald, Molly 31, 41, 72
"Rock Hard" 17
Rolling Stone 29, 47, 57, 77
"Root Down" 61
Roxy, The 14, 76
Rubin, Rick 11, 14, 16–17, 26, 30, 31, 32, 33, 36, 38, 39, 41, 46, 47, 54, 78, 88
Rudin, Scott 32
Run DMC 18, 20, 26, 27, 30, 78, 88
"Sabotage" 61, 63–4, 69, 88
"Sabrosa" 61
Santigold 80, 82
Scared Shitless 32
"Scenario" 29, 45
Schellenbach, Kate 13, 16, 56, 58, 88
"Scoop, The" 61, 63
Scilken, Davis 56
"Shadrach" 35
"Shake Your Rump" 35, 38, 41, 46
"Shambala" 61, 68
"Shazam" 75
"She's Crafty" 25
"She's On It" 20, 26
Shocklee, Hank 41, 45

Simmons, Joey 18
Simmons, Russell 17, 18–20, 26, 27, 31, 32–3, 36, 45, 46, 47, 85
Skye, Ione 41, 72
"Slow And Low" 25
"Slow Ride" 25
Smith, Joe 39, 48
"Sneakin' Out The Hospital" 75
"So What'cha Want" 51, 53, 57
Some Old Bullshit 888
"Something's Got To Give" 51
"Song For Junior" 75
"Song For The Man" 75
"Sounds of Science, The" 35
Source, The 57
Spin 41, 47, 77
"Stand Together" 51
"Stop That Train" 46
Strummer, Joe 8
Sugarhill Gang 13, 78
"Super Disco Breakin'" 75, 78
"Sure Shot" 61, 63
"That's It That's All" 75
Three Feet High And Rising 47
"3 The Hard Way" 75
"Three Mc's And One DJ" 75
"3-Minute Rule" 35, 45, 48
"Time for Livin'" 51, 537
"Time To Build" 79
"Time To Get III" 25
"To All The Girls" 35
To The Five Boroughs 75, 79, 89
"Too Many Rappers" 81–2
"Tough Guy" 61
"Transitions" 61
"Triple Trouble" 75
"Unite" 75
"Update, The" 61
Velvet Underground 13
Village Voice, The 29, 57
Wangdu, Dechen 72, 82, 89
"We Got Th" 75
"What Comes Around" 35, 46
White House 45
Whodini 26
Winfrey, Oprah 27, 29
Yauch, Frances 17, 82
Yauch, Tenzin 82
"(You Gotta) Fight For Your Right (To Party!)" 25, 29, 30, 37, 56, 63, 72, 81, 82, 88, 89

CREDITS

The publishers would like to thank the following sources for their kind permission to reproduce the pictures in this book.

Key, t=top, l=left, r=right, c=centre, b=bottom

1. Mirrorpix, 3. © Sunny Bak, 4-5. Getty Images/Paul Natkin/WireImage, 6. Getty Images/Michael Ochs Archives, 7. Getty Images/Chris Walter/WireImage, 9-10. © Sunny Bak, 12. Topfoto/The Image Works, 13. Getty Images/Janette Beckman, 14. Pymca.com/Josh Cheuse, 15. Corbis/Lynn Goldsmith, 16. Pymca.com/Josh Cheuse, 17. Corbis/Paul Rider/Retna Ltd., 18. Getty Images/Janette Beckman, 19. Pymca.com/Josh Cheuse, 20. Corbis/Lynn Goldsmith, 20-21. Pymca.com/Josh Cheuse, 22. Getty Images/Michael Ochs Archive, 23t. Rex Features/Andre Csillag, 23b. Photoshot/Starstock, 24. Corbis/Laura Levine, 26. Alamy/Lewton Cole, 27-29. © Sunny Bak, 30. Getty Images/Ebet Roberts/Redferns, 31. Corbis/Scott Weiner/Retna Ltd., 32. Mirrorpix, 33t. Rex Features/Ilpo Musto, 33b. Photoshot/Erick Heinila/Idols, 34. Photoshot/Andy Freeberg, 36. Getty Images/Paul Natkin/WireImage, 37. Getty Images/Kevin Cummins, 38. Rex Features/Ilpo Musto, 39tl. Getty Images/Ebet Roberts/Redferns, 39tr. Getty Images/Ron Galella, Ltd./WireImage, 39b. Getty Images/Tony Buckingham/Reuters, 40. Corbis Outline/Raul Vega, 41. Topfoto/UPP, 42. Getty Images/Michael Ochs Archives, 43t. Photoshot/Robin Kaplan, 43b. Photoshot/Fie Knaeps, 44. Getty Images/Kevin Cummins, 45. Photoshot/Larry Busacca, 46. Photoshot/LFI, 48. Getty Images/Time & Life Pictures, 49. Getty Images/Denis O'Regan, 50. Corbis Outline/Sue Kwon, 52. Getty Images/Ebet Roberts/Redferns, 53. Photoshot/LFI, 54. Getty Images/Ebet Roberts/Redferns, 55t. Getty Images/Kevin Cummins, 55b. Photoshot/LFI, 56t. Corbis/Chi Modu/Diverse Images, 56b. Photoshot/LFI, 57. Getty Images/Denis O'Regan, 58. Corbis Outline/Shawn Mortensen, 59. Corbis Outline/Jeffrey Thurnher, 60. Getty Images/NBCU Photo Bank via Getty Images, 62. Getty Images/L.Busacca/WireImage, 63t. Corbis Outline/Stephen Stickler, 63b. Rex Features/Brian Rasic, 64. Rex Features, 65. Corbis/Catherine Bauknight/Zuma, 66. Getty Images/Michael Ochs Archives, 67t. Mirrorpix, 67b. Topfoto/UPP, 68. Corbis/Tim Mosenfelder, 69. Getty Images/Tim Mosenfelder, 70l. Photoshot, 70r. Rex Features/Brian Rasic, 71. Getty Images/Michel Linssen/Redferns, 72l. Getty Images/Ben Hider, 72c. Rex Features/Araldo Di Crollalanza, 72r. Getty Images/Astrid Stawiarz/Getty Images for NOWNESS, 73. Getty Images/David Tonge, 74. Getty Images/Danny Clinch, 76-77. Photoshot, 78t, Corbis/Marc Serota/Reuters, 78b-79. Getty Images/Mick Hutson/Redferns, 80. Rex Features/Justin Lloyd/Newspix, 81t. Getty Images/Michael Ochs Archives, 81b. Photoshot, 82t. Corbis/Marko Djurica/Reuters, 82b. Corbis/Hector Acevedo/Zuma Press, 83. Rex/Unimedia Images, 84. Getty Images/Jeff Kravitz/FilmMagic, 85. Rex Features/Mantel/Sipa Press, 86. Photoshot, 87. Corbis Outline/Michael Wong, 90. Corbis/Lynn Goldsmith, 92-93. Photoshot, 95l. Getty Images/John Lamparski, 95r. Getty Images/Jeff Kravitz/FilmMagic, 96. Corbis Outline/Jerome Albertini

Every effort has been made to acknowledge correctly and contact the source and/or copyright holder of each picture and Carlton Books Limited apologises for any unintentional errors or omissions, which will be corrected in future editions of this book.

RIGHT: Despite MCA being too ill to attend the induction, the Beastie Boys enter the Rock and Roll Hall of Fame, 2012.

NEXT PAGE: "Three Idiots," 2004. The Beastie Boys—one of the most critically acclaimed, and popular, musical acts of all time.

BEASTIE BOYS
ROCK AND ROLL HALL OF FAME
INDUCTED
2012
CLEVELAND · OHIO
PRESENTED BY:
MANISHA & NEIL
SETHI